A HANDLIST
OF THE
TOPOGRAPHICAL PRINTS OF CLWYD
(Denbighshire, Flintshire and Edeyrnion)

compiled by
DERRICK PRATT
and
A.G. VEYSEY

CLWYD RECORD OFFICE
1977

Published by

CLWYD RECORD OFFICE
THE OLD RECTORY, HAWARDEN
DEESIDE, CH5 3NR

Printed in the Administration and Legal Services Department,
Clwyd County Council

ISBN 0 904444 14 7

CLWYD COUNTY COUNCIL

FOREWORD

by Councillor K. Iball, JP
Chairman of the Cultural, Libraries and Recreation Committee

Since the establishment of the Flintshire Record Office in 1951, the collecting of topographical prints of the county, together with original water-colours, drawings, photographs and postcards, has been an important feature of its work. These are among the most frequently consulted records at Hawarden. Following local government reorganisation and the formation of the new county of Clwyd, prints (and photographs) of Denbighshire are also being acquired, and a growing number are now available for research at the Record Office's branch office at 46 Clwyd Street, Ruthin. The Clwyd Record Office depends very much on the generosity and public-spiritedness of owners of such historically valuable illustrative material, who deposit it on loan in the county archives and therefore make it available for research.

Prints have become a prominent feature of antique dealers' displays. They are often the oldest possession on the walls of many modern homes. I hope that this list compiled by the Record Office will be of interest not only to the students of the landscape and the social and economic history of North-East Wales, but to collectors and those who wish to know something more of these visual records of the past of our county.

Kenneth Iball

October 1977

CONTENTS

EDITORIAL NOTE

This list of topographical prints of Clwyd is the second in the series of Record Office Handlists. The first, a *Handlist of Denbigh Borough Records,* was published in May 1975. These handlists are intended to provide students with information on important classes of records preserved by the Clwyd Record Office in its headquarters at the Old Rectory, Hawarden, and branch office at 46 Clwyd Street, Ruthin.

A list of topographical prints of Flintshire was compiled by Mr. Derrick Pratt and published in the Flintshire Historical Society's *Journal,* Vol. 22 (1965-6). Mr. Pratt accepted an invitation to compile similar checklists of prints for Denbighshire and the former Edeyrnion district of Merioneth, which, together with Flintshire, form the new county of Clwyd. Many of the prints were first identified in the *Catalogue of Welsh Topographical Prints* published by the National Museum of Wales in 1926.

The opportunity has been taken to revise the Flintshire list and a number of additions have been made. Record Office holdings are marked in the text. The majority of the prints can be seen in the Department of Prints and Drawings at the National Library of Wales, Aberystwyth, while a large collection is also held in the Department of Art at the National Museum of Wales in Cardiff.

For the purposes of this list, a topographical print has been defined as a full or half-page engraving of a landscape or scene, produced and sold as an illustration in its own right, or having provenance in a published topographical work from which it has been subsequently removed. Illustrations which are an integral part of letterpress have been omitted, but some very small prints, to be found, for example, in G.N. Wright's *Scenes in North Wales* (1833), have been included, and also line engravings which are obviously vignettes from printed maps. With a few exceptions only, the list does not include prints published after 1900.

The exact title of each print has been given, preserving peculiarities of spelling. The entries are arranged generally in alphabetical order, although this has sometimes been neglected to keep prints of the same subject together. Measurements of the engraved surface are in millimetres, and the printing process, details of artists, engraver, printer, publisher and date are stated where possible. Titles of topographical works in which the print is included are listed where known, but corrections and any additional information would be welcomed by the Record Office. Variations in titles, engravers' names, etc., have been noted wherever possible, as plates were often used for many years and could be re-touched or re-worked.

It has been assumed, for convenience, that Clwyd comprises the entire ancient counties of Flintshire and Denbighshire, with the Edeyrnion district of Merioneth. Since 1974, six Denbighshire parishes in the Conwy Valley, including Llanrwst (nos. 270-96), have formed part of the new administrative county of Gwynedd. The list is based only on the holdings of the Record Office, the National Library and National Museum of Wales, and two private collections in the county. The numbering is consecutive, although gaps have been left to allow for additions and corrections. As a rule, Flintshire prints are held in the Record Office at Hawarden, Denbighshire and Edeyrnion prints at Ruthin.

CRO   Denotes a print available in the Record Office.

CRO*   No loose copy of the print is held, but it is to be found in a topographical work in the search-room library at Hawarden.

CL   The print is included in a topographical work held in the County Library Headquarters at Mold.

INTRODUCTION

The recent publication of *Clwyd in Old Photographs* focussed attention on the fact that, in addition to its large collection of documents, the Record Office also possesses a considerable corpus of graphic material — original drawings, engraved prints, picture post-cards, photographs, etc. — that help to illustrate many aspects of life in the county over the last 250 years.

The photographic collection numbers more than 6,000 items, the earliest dating from *c.* 1860. To depict landscape, life and manners prior to this date, the researcher must have resource to engraved prints — woodcuts, line engravings, lithographs, aquatints, and etchings. Within this category of graphic material, topographical prints are by far the most numerous. While Clwyd may not be amongst the best represented areas of the Principality in this respect, there are nevertheless over 1,000 topographical prints in existence relating to Flintshire, Denbighshire and the former Rural District of Edeyrnion.

With the exception of two or three line engravings of St. Asaph Cathedral and St. Winefride's Well, which were published between 1656 and 1720, accompanying such pioneer works as Daniel King's *Cathedral and Conventual Churches of England and Wales* (1656), and the print of Wrexham Church (1705-8), most of the prints belong to the period 1770-1850, the golden age of British engraving. They are of very unequal artistic merit, and are perhaps more indicative of a concern for form, shape, and colour rather than of an eye for exact topographical detail. However the individuality and artistic quality which are the distinctive but charming characteristics of such old prints, make them much sought after by collectors.

Today the function of the topographical artist and engraver has been partially replaced by photography. Although the eighteenth-century artist and engraver could not compete with the precise eye of the modern camera in achieving accuracy and verisimilitude, this should not lead one to decry these early craftsmen, or to despise the topographical print as a valuable source of information for the local historian. To persist in such an attitude would be as illogical as to despise Caxton's printing press because it did not achieve all that modern presses and typographical processes have done.

The prints of Clwyd reveal a countryside and landscape virtually lost to the present day inhabitant of the county, being a record of Clwyd before the Industrial Revolution had drastically affected the character and distribution of the population and had initiated a process that has seen the disappearance of many buildings of historical interest, the despoliation of scenery and the creation of new industrial areas.

However, from the point of view of the industrial archaeologist, it is disappointing to discover that, although the eastern part of Clwyd is underlain by the Coal Measures and the mineralised belt of the Carboniferous Limestone, less than a dozen prints — discounting those depicting water mills at Denbigh, Erbistock, Llangollen, Marford and Ruthin, or the viaducts and aqueducts over the Dee and Ceiriog — illustrate the early commercial and industrial development of Deeside and the Buckley, Wrexham and Chirk areas. Several prints depict copper and brass works and cotton mills on the Holywell Stream; one print shows the huge, ancient waterwheel at Sir Roger Mostyn's 'colework' which so much intrigued the Duke of Beaufort in 1684, while an aquatint by Thomas Cartwright, 1814, possibly proves that horse-drawn barge traffic did after all use the short three-mile stretch of the Ffrwd branch of the Ellesmere Canal before it was finally abandoned. One lithograph shows a Mold of pleasing proportions, about 1865, although surrounded by coal mines, while the solitary print of Acrefair depicts a primitive horse-gin or pit-head winding gear alongside a very rustic, half-timbered, thatched cottage. The sporadic occurrence of prints on an industrial theme contrasts markedly with, for example, the numerous prints between 1800 and 1860 that illustrate the growth of the slate industry in Caernarvonshire.

Again, it must be realised that the figure of just over 1,000 prints for Clwyd is relative, easily exceeding the number for Powys, but being only 40% of the total number relating to the adjacent county of Gwynedd, with the former county of Caernarvonshire alone accounting for some 1,050 prints. This general paucity of prints for Clwyd can be explained by the fact that the county as a whole has little affinity with the rugged terrain and natural scenic splendour of Caernarvonshire and Merioneth that so captured the imagination of tourists in the late-eighteenth and early-nineteenth centuries.

For any young gentleman with worthwhile social aspirations, the 'grand tour' of Europe or an extended sojourn in Italy had long been considered an essential part of their education, but, possibly in the backwash of the great Romantic movement of the eighteenth century, and certainly because of the unsettled conditions on the continent during the French Revolution and the Napoleonic era, Snowdon and Cader Idris, the Scottish Highlands, the Lake District and the south-west all witnessed a steadily increasing influx of tourists, mainly members of the nobility and gentry; and prints of those regions make the few scenes we have of the Clwydian Range and the Denbigh Moors look very ordinary, monotonous, and almost unattractive by comparison.

Further, in making for Snowdonia, the majority of tourists used the Shrewsbury-Llangollen-Corwen-Holyhead coach road, which, after 1800, eclipsed the coast route along the Dee estuary and the Chester-Holyhead post road. As early as 1769, the latter had been described as 'in several places frequently overflowed, in general very narrow and incommodious, and cannot be effectively amended and kept in repair by the ordinary course of the law'. Not surprisingly, therefore, over 190 of the topographical prints listed below depict scenes in the Vale of Llangollen — Dinas Brân, Plas Newydd, Pontcysyllte Aqueduct, Valle Crucis, the Eglwyseg Rocks, and along the Dee both above and below Llangollen. Here where the ravages of time have done little to soften the harsh contours, and where the Dee has cut a splendid gorge through a barrier of Carboniferous Limestone, the tourist was given a foretaste of the scenic splendours that awaited him if he cared to penetrate further into Wales, and was perhaps tempted to loiter awhile. Two centuries ago, as at the present time, the countryside about Llangollen was sufficiently unspoilt and 'different' to attract tourists in ever increasing numbers.

Apart from the occasional foray up the Aled and upper Clwyd valleys, or an equally adventurous excursion up the Tanat valley from Oswestry to Pistyll Rhaeadr, 'that great cataract in North Wales', tourists seem to have paid scant attention to Mynydd Hiraethog or the area lying to the south of Llangollen, embracing the Ceiriog valley and the northern extremities of the Berwyns. This, to some extent, was due to the fact that such areas lacked adequate roads and means of communication. He would have been a brave adventurer who sought to penetrate the Welsh fastness as far as Llanarmon Dyffryn Ceiriog, or even beyond, to the waterfalls at Dolydd Ceiriog! One must also appreciate the sentiments of Edward Pugh, author of *Cambria Depicta* (1816), when he wrote of 'the difficulty in which a stranger unaquainted with the Welsh Language or the country involved himself the moment he quitted the high roads and plunged into the intricacies of the mountains'.

While much of the scenery of Flintshire and Denbighshire presented a relatively familiar vista to the English eye, topographical boredom was fortunately relieved by many features of historical and architectural interest. Rhuddlan, Flint, Denbigh, Chirk, Dinas Brân and Hawarden Castles were drawn from almost every angle. By contrast one must attribute the few prints of Holt, Caergwrle, Ruthin, Gwrych and Ewloe Castles, if not to the relative isolation of such places, then to the scantiness of material remains, or to the comparative disinterest in newly-erected pseudo-Gothic piles.

Outside George Cuitt's etchings of Welsh 'hovels' in Holywell, there are very few examples of domestic architecture. Most of the important houses of the local gentry are represented, however, by one or two prints — Acton Park, Broughton Hall, Brynkinalt, Dyffryn Aled, Erddig, Lleweni, Leeswood Hall, Plas Teg, Rug and Wynnstay. Such prints, especially those obviously based on architects' original drawings, are of great importance to the social and local historian in that many of these historic houses have since been demolished, destroyed by fire or extensively restored. Paul Gauci's lithographs of Bryn Asaph, Talacre Hall, and the Deanery House, St. Asaph — all the designs of Thomas Jones, the Chester architect — come immediately to mind.

Basingwerk Abbey, St.Asaph Cathedral, St.Winefride's Well and Valle Crucis Abbey are well represented, but many other churches, amongst them Nannerch, Penley, Llandysilio, Llansilin, Ruthin, Whitford, and Whitewell (Iscoyd), and the Friaries at Denbigh and Rhuddlan, are illustrated only by a single print. Again, while ecclesiastical buildings generally seem to have merited little attention from the topographical artist, many of the prints which do exist are of the architect's original drawings or, as in the case of Erbistock, Hawarden, Penley and Flint, depict the immediate predecessors to existing churches or show churches prior to alteration or restoration — in several instances, after disastrous fires. Thus, despite some confusion over dates, David Cox's painting of Penley Church would appear to depict the original chapel-of-ease to Ellesmere built about 1560, the first of three churches on the same site. Wrexham lay on the Chester-Shrewsbury coach road, and both artist and tourist evidently thought it worthwhile to break their journey to visit and sketch the parish church which is the subject of, or dominates, most of the topographical prints of that town.

Many of the tourists who visited North Wales were evidently gentlemen of leisure or considerable means, who afterwards recorded their impressions in writing. Often they were themselves competent amateur artists, illustrating their journals with pen and pencil sketches and water-colours. Others, lacking ability, or being more wealthy, employed professional artists to accompany them on their travels. Thus Thomas Pennant (1726-98) of Downing, the noted naturalist, antiquary and traveller, was accompanied on his tours of North Wales between 1769 and 1790 by Caernarvonshire-born artist Moses Griffith (1747-1819). Described by Pennant as 'an able artist', many of his originals are to be seen in the Record Office at Hawarden, and the Grosvenor Museum, Chester, as well as the National Library and National Museum of Wales. Some of his drawings of Clwyd scenes were engraved by such eminent engravers as Peter Mazell and William Angus — in the *Tour in Wales* (1778), and for the *History of Whiteford and Holywell*, written only two years before Pennant's death. A few were engraved originally for John Boydell, Cheapside, London, and later appeared in Sir Richard Colt Hoare's *A Collection of Forty-Eight Views of Noblemen's and Gentlemen's Seats &c.* (1795). He also illustrated with the original water-colours the special edition of Pennant's *Tour* now in the National Library.

Numerous accounts of tours in North Wales were published, either as simple printed narratives or as composite volumes where the descriptive text is intimately bound up with engraved views. It is from these volumes that most of the prints offered for sale in dealers' shops or auction rooms have been torn. In addition to Pennant's works mentioned above, the works most frequently cited in the catalogue of prints below are Edward Pugh, *Cambria Depicta: A Tour Through North Wales* (1816), William Cathrall, *A History of North Wales* (1828), Jones & Co., *Wales Illustrated* (1830), George Cuitt, *Etchings of Ancient Buildings in the City of Chester, Castles in North Wales & Other Miscellaneous Subjects* (1816, reprinted 1855), and Thomas Roscoe, *Wanderings and Excursions in North Wales* (1836). A number of prints were published singly by such firms as Rock & Co., and Newman & Co., London, or in volumes without any printed text such as Henry Grueber's *Six Lithographic Views of Seats in the Neighbourhood of Wrexham, North Wales* (Acton Park, Gwersyllt Park, Trevalyn Hall, Wynnstay, Gwernhaylod, Hawarden Castle) and J.G. Wood's *Six Views in the Neighbourhood of Llangollen and Bala* (1793). The firm of John Newman & Co., lithographers and line engravers, is worthy of special mention in that its artists and engravers were responsible for a good proportion of the prints listed below, particularly the prints of Rhyl and district. The town was fast developing into an important seaside resort, the visitors to which looked for small prints as mementoes, even as today's visitors buy the modern picture postcard. These small line engravings were sold, if not indeed commissioned, by local stationers and even chemists. Some were bound into omnibus volumes — *Views in*

Wales, Views of Mold & Neighbourhood, Seventy-two Views of North Wales and so on —
while others were incorporated into handy guide books such as W. Davis's *Hand-Book for
the Vale of Clwyd* (1856), and D. Lewis's *Visitor's Guide to Rhyl and its Vicinity* (1852).

Some artists, on the other hand, engraved and published their own works, for example,
William Crane of Chester, brother of the more celebrated Thomas Crane, who is represented
in the following list by lithographs of Chirk Castle, Hawarden Castle and Rectory, Llangollen,
Plas Newydd, Rhual, St.Winefride's Well, Talacre Hall, Valle Crucis Abbey, and the parish
church of Wrexham. Most prominent in this category, however, are the line engravings by
the brothers Samuel and Nathaniel Buck *(fl.* 1726-53). North Wales was very much within
their orbit, and they made drawings and engravings of Caergwrle, Chirk, Denbigh, Dinas
Brân, Flint, Holt, Hawarden, Ruthin, and Rhuddlan Castles, Denbigh Friary, Rhuddlan
Priory, and Valle Crucis and Basingwerk Abbeys, which they published in *Views of all the
Castles in the Principality of Wales* (1742). They all conform to an immediately recognisable
pattern — long horizontally drawn pictures, with, underneath, an inscription containing
topographical detail about the picture and subject, with the artists' names and date of
engraving. These formal, heavy engravings compare strangely with the fine delicate pen and
ink work and colour wash of the original drawings, which are to be seen in both the
National Library and the National Museum of Wales.

Two of the most eminent engravers, printsellers, and publishers of the eighteenth
century had strong personal connections with Flintshire and with the village of Hawarden in
particular; yet it is strange that Clwyd as a whole is represented only by twenty-one prints
that were either engraved or commissioned and published by them. John Boydell (1719-
1804) was born at Dorrington, near Wem, Shropshire; he is often considered a native of
Hawarden, where his father was bailiff to Sir John Glynne. In 1739 he came under the
influence of Thomas Badeslade and William Harry Toms, who were in Flintshire and
Denbighshire to make sketches for their large engravings of Chirk Castle, Erddig, and
Hawarden Castle and Park, and the following year he was apprenticed to Toms.

In 1749 John Boydell began business in London as an engraver and publisher on his
own account. He published a series of 152 topographical views of England and Wales which
were put into portfolios and sold at five guineas each — represented in Clwyd by views of
Denbigh, Hawarden and Rhuddlan Castles, Holywell and Wrexham parish church. Later he
pioneered great publishing enterprises, notably the Shakespeare Gallery, commissioning
famous artists and employing a large number of expert engravers. Between 1773 and 1795
artists such as J. Ingleby, Paul Sandby, and Moses Griffith, and engravers such as W.C.
Wilson, W. Watts and G. Barret were commissioned to produce views of Cynwyd, Dyffryn
Aled, Llannerch, Mostyn Hall, Lleweni, Greenfield, Rhuddlan and Hawarden Castles,
Holywell and elsewhere. Boydell became an Alderman and Lord Mayor of London in 1790.
The extent of his operations as a print publisher may be best gauged by the fact that he
published prints taken from no fewer than 4,432 engraved copper plates, representing an
expenditure of over £350,000. His manuscript autobiography is among the Bell Jones MSS.
in the Record Office [1]. Boydell's nephew, Josiah, son of Samuel Boydell of the Manor House,
Hawarden, also became celebrated as an engraver and painter, exhibiting at the Royal
Academy between 1772 and 1779, and entering into partnership with his uncle.

Surprisingly, perhaps, most members of the rapidly-developing British school of landscape painting visited Flintshire and Denbighshire. Numerous paintings and drawings by
Richard Wilson, dating from the period 1760-71, depict Northop church and village, and
scenes in the Dee valley at Holt, Eaton Hall, Wynnstay and Llangollen, but only one Clwyd
scene was ever engraved — a solitary lithograph by W.P. Sherlock *(fl.* 1801-28) of Dinas Brân
with Llangollen bridge and mill in the middle ground, the original of which is now in the F.
Penfold Hyland Collection, Sydney, Australia. J.M.W. Turner (1775-1851) fared slightly
better and is represented in the catalogue by five line engravings of Flint, Flint Castle,
Llangollen and Valle Crucis Abbey by J. Walker, T. Tagg, J.C. Varrall and James H. Kernot,

[1]See *Flintshire Historical Society Journal,* Vol. II (1925), pp.79-87.

the last engraver being also responsible for the illustrations which are the redeeming feature of *The Poems of Felicia Hemans* (1858). Julius Caesar Ibbetson (1759-1817) visited North Wales *c.* 1790-5; and aquatints of scenes painted at Pengwern near Rhuddlan, and in the Vale of Llangollen, were made by J. Bluck, himself a landscape painter of no mean repute, who exhibited at the Royal Academy between 1791 and 1819.

J. Varley and David Cox, both contemporaries of Turner, are represented in the following list. But even better known, from the point of view of the number of engravings made of his works, is Paul Sandby (1725-1809), a noted landscape and architectural painter, who was amongst the first in England to practise aquatint engraving. He published a series of engravings in *Twelve Views in North Wales* (1776), which included views of Chirk Castle, Valle Crucis Abbey, Overton Bridge, and Wynnstay. Between 1776 and 1786, Sandby produced prints of Dinas Brân, Cynwyd, Llanrwst, Llangollen and the Dee valley, while his paintings of Newbridge, Wynnstay and Valle Crucis were translated into line engravings by Peter Mazell, M.A. Rooker and T. Morris for *Select Views in Great Britain &c.* (1781), and C. Hulbert's *History and Description of the County of Salop*, published as late as 1837. Almost as prolific as Sandby, but perhaps less well known, was Thomas Walmsley (1763-1805), who worked as a scene painter at Covent Garden and exhibited at the Royal Academy between 1790 and 1796. Thirteen of his Clwyd landscapes were realised in a magnificent series of large aquatints by F. Jukes, sold separately as they were published between May 1793 and June 1794, and then issued in a composite volume of *Welsh Views*, (1794). Walmsley seems not to have strayed from the well-worn path of the regular tourist. A list of his works — Overton Bridge, Erbistock Church and Mill, Acrefair, Nant-y-belan, Llangollen Bridge, Pentrefelin, Corwen, Llandrillo and Crogen — serves to emphasise the importance of the Dee valley as a means of access to the remoter parts of Wales. Other aquatint engravers — Thomas Cartwright, John Hill — continued to produce prints of Walmsley's work (e.g. Ruabon and Pontnewydd, St. Asaph) for some time after his death.

Other names spring to mind — George Cuitt, Edward Dayes, pupil of Turner and Cox, Henry Gastineau (particularly prolific), J.P. Neale, David Parkes. The list is a long one, and, excluding all the anonymous prints in the following list – engravings made by anonymous craftsmen after equally anonymous artists — well over eighty artists can be said to have visited Flintshire and Denbighshire and to have had their works engraved, thus reaching a wider public.

According to the process involved in their production, the prints listed below are classified as either line engravings, aquatints, wood engravings, lithographs, or etchings. Only occasionally is a combination of processes found — an etching/stipple engraving or aquatint/etching. A small number of photo-lithographs date from the closing decades of the nineteenth century.

The majority of Clwyd prints are line engravings, this being the process most commonly used on account of its relative cheapness. A 'mirror' picture is first drawn upon a polished plate of metal (initially copper, later steel, which was more durable and less susceptible to damage), and the lines incised with a 'graver' and the rough, raised edges removed. Only the engraved lines hold ink and these are the only part of the plate to print. The controlled use of cross-hatching and parallel lines produce different tones and light and shade effect. While work produced by such a mechanical process may not possess the finer aesthetic qualities present in etchings and aquatint engravings, the early copper plate engravings of Francis Place, J. Harris and Daniel King possess a clarity and simplicity often lacking in later work.

Wood engraving is represented in the following list mainly by the work of Hugh Hughes (1790-1863) — Valle Crucis and Basingwerk Abbeys, Moel Famau, Rhaeadr Cynwyd, Gresford and Mold churches, Rhuddlan Castle, St. Asaph Cathedral, St. Winefride's Well — ten of the sixty woodcuts that illustrate his *Beauties of Cambria* (1823), along with isolated wood engravings to illustrate such works as W. Cathrall's *History of North Wales* (1828).

11

This process corresponds to the method of printing from type. The picture is drawn in reverse on the surface of the wood block. Those parts of the design intended to print white are cut away by a knife or graver. The black lines are left in relief.

There are just over sixty etchings in the following list of topographical prints. Many, like W.M. Craig's fictitious, highly imaginative rendering of a gate-house and draw-bridge at Castell Dinas Brân, are crudely executed, but therein, perhaps, lies their greater fascination and added attraction. Fifteen etchings of Clwyd scenes illustrate J.G. Wood's *The Principal Rivers of Wales* (1813). Wood is better served by Maria Prestel's aquatints based on his drawings of scenes in the Dee and Ceirw valleys which he published in *Six Views in the Neighbourhood of Llangollen and Bala* (1793). Much more polished are George Cuitt's prints of Denbigh Castle, Llanrwst church and various facets of vernacular architecture in Holywell, which grace his *Etchings of Ancient Buildings* (1816) and *Wanderings and Pencillings amongst the Ruins of Olden Times* (1855). A. Clint's six etchings in and about Llangollen illustrate G.J. Bennett's *A Pedestrian Tour Through North Wales* (1838). In etching the plate (usually copper or zinc) is coated with a wax-like substance called the ground, which, when dry, is drawn or scratched upon with a steel needle. The plate is then immersed in a bath of nitric acid which bites into the copper opened up along the scratched lines. Subsequently the plate is washed to remove the ground, which has resisted the action of the acid.

Generally woodcuts, line engravings and etchings are all lacking in tone. Aquatint on the other hand is the etching process which gives the nearest approach that prints can ever offer to the original drawings. However, the delicacy, precision, and subtle tone effects of such prints are only achieved by the most complicated and demanding of the engraving processes. This explains why only some hundred or more Clwyd scenes are depicted by this process and why, significantly, over half of these are attributable to a select body of aquatint engravers, masters of their technique — Paul Sandby, Francis Jukes, Thomas Cartwright, J. Bluck, Samuel Alken and Maria C. Prestel. Sandby's characteristic monotone aquatints are difficult to distinguish from original sepia drawings. Francis Jukes and William Daniell (the latter represented only by a print of Point of Ayr lighthouse) produced coloured aquatints closely resembling original water-colours, but it should be realised that such prints rarely received more than two or three colours applied on the plate, colouring being largely done afterwards on the print itself. As the name implies, in the aquatint process not lines but areas are bitten by the acid *(aqua fortis)* and the result is an imitation of washes by water-colour. The perfect, subtle gradation of tints is obtained by a staged process of successively 'stopping out' and biting, those parts of the plate subjected to the greatest number of acid baths holding most ink and therefore printing as the darkest portions of the finished print.

Unlike the relief or intaglio processes already referred to, lithography is a surface printing process whereby impressions are obtained by contact with a flat stone (or occasionally a metal plate) which has been able to retain the ink. The art of lithography was invented by a German, Aloys Senefelder (1771-1834), who was not an artist but a printer. In Britain the process rapidly gained in popularity and commercial use, particularly from about 1820, due mainly to the efforts of such pioneers as Charles Hullmandel (1789-1850), who is represented in the accompanying list both by his own lithographs — Denbigh, and Chirk and Pontcysyllte Aqueducts — and as the printer of lithographs by other artists. Better represented is Louis Haghe (1806-85), a Belgian lithographer and water-colour painter, who came to London as a young man. He eventually joined William Day in the firm of Day & Haghe, lithographers, who printed several views of seats, ecclesiastical and public buildings in Clwyd — Brinkinalt, Denbigh Hospital, Valle Crucis Abbey, Wrexham Church, Flint Town Hall and Market, etc. — for enterprising stationers and print sellers in Oswestry, Wrexham and Chester.

Specific illustrations of the various methods of engraving now follow, but the task of choosing prints from the large number available has not been easy. Some consideration has been given to geographical location, the eminence of the artist, the importance of the engraver, and to the date of the prints. It is hoped that the resulting selection combines topographical interest with artistic merit.

ACKNOWLEDGEMENTS

Thanks are due to Mr. M.L. Timothy, Keeper of Prints and Drawings at the National Library of Wales, and his staff, especially Miss Gwyneth Lewis, Senior Research Assistant, and to Mr. Peter Hughes, Acting Keeper of the Department of Art at the National Museum of Wales, for producing the prints from their collections, and for generous assistance with many queries. Lord Kenyon and Mr. Tom Lloyd-Roberts were both keenly interested in this project, and the Record Office is indebted to them for making their collections available during the compilation of the list. Mr. D. Leslie Davies kindly allowed his print of Wrexham Church (no. 520) to be reproduced for the handlist. Mr. E. Hughes and the staff of the Reference Section of the Clwyd Library Service produced books and checked bibliographies with efficiency and promptness. The cover was designed in the Graphics Section of the County Planning Department with the assistance of Mr. W.A. Boswell and Mr. C.B. Wharton; and the photographic work of Mr. B. Hamilton of the Educational Technology Centre is also gratefully acknowledged. The publication has benefited from the interest and expertise of Mr. L. Sullivan and his colleagues in the County Council's Reprographic Section. The index has been compiled by Mr. C.J. Williams, Deputy County Archivist.

NOTES ON THE ILLUSTRATIONS

1. DENBIGH
    This view of Denbigh, with its charming hunting scene, is by John Boydell (1719-1804), who was responsible for a number of the more interesting prints of Clwyd. The print shows the castle and abbey together with St. Hilary's church, and the ruins (on the left) of the imposing unfinished church which was begun in the second half of the sixteenth century by Robert Dudley, Earl of Leicester, and which was intended to replace the cathedral at St. Asaph.

2. MEETING OF THE ROYAL BRITISH BOWMEN, ERDDIG
    An aquatint by W.J. Bennett (1787-c.1830) after James Townshend, a lesser nineteenth-century landscape painter. The Society of the Royal British Bowmen was established in 1787 by Sir Foster Cunliffe, Bart., of Acton Hall. By the end of the eighteenth century, archery had become a fashionable recreation amongst the gentry and aristocracy. Members of the Society, which enjoyed the patronage of the Prince of Wales, and later that of William IV, met at different mansions in turn, and competed for prizes. The Society ceased to function in 1794 owing to the exigencies of war; it was revived for a short time during the peace of 1802-3 and again in 1818, being finally dissolved in 1880. The print depicts the meeting at Erddig Hall on 13 September 1822.

3. WEST VIEW OF VALLE CRUCIS ABBEY
    A line engraving by Samuel and Nathaniel Buck, 1742. Samuel Buck (1696-1779) was one of the most prolific of eighteenth-century topographical artists and engravers, publishing between 1711 and 1753 over 500 views of ruined abbeys, castles and towns in England and Wales. From 1727 to 1753, during which period eighteen prints of Clwyd scenes were published, he was assisted by his brother Nathaniel. Their prints are noted for their accuracy and architectural detail. This is the earliest engraving of this much-illustrated ancient monument, which provided the subject for at least one picture by almost every artist who visited Denbighshire in the eighteenth and nineteenth centuries. Valle Crucis was a poor house and the buildings were on a small scale. Buck's print shows the east calustral range roofless and ruinous, and it remained so until c. 1800 when the dorter and adjacent chambers were once more converted into a farm-house.

4. CHIRK VIADUCT
    A lithograph by G. Hawkins (1819-52) after a drawing by George Pickering (1794-1857), illustrator of Ormerod's *History of Cheshire*, who succeeded George Cuitt as a drawing master at Chester. The massive civil-engineering works associated with the spread of canals and railways frequently caught the eye of the topographical artist. This engraving, published by T. Catherall of Chester c. 1850, is accurate in detail, the viewpoint being somewhere on the Pontfaen-Trehowell road. The viaduct took eighteen months to complete (1846-8). Henry Robertson was the engineer; the actual builder was Thomas Brassey. The first train over the viaduct was a ballast train on 2 October 1848.

5. TOWN AND VALE OF LLANGOLLEN
    A lithograph by G. Hawkins after G. Pickering, published by T. Catherall, Chester, c. 1840. This view up the Dee valley is from somewhere on Pen-y-coed. St. Collen's Church, the bridge, and Dinas Brân are useful orientating landmarks. Very few houses line the Holyhead road. North of the river the (Lower) Dee mills stand out. Built in 1805 as a cotton factory, it switched in 1843 to the production of flannel and woollens. The Upper Dee Mill, built in 1855, is absent, but the end of the cotton-spinning mill (now cottages), rebuilt after the fire in 1814, is visible, thus dating the print approximately.

6. BLEACH WORKS AT LLEWENI
A line engraving, dated 1792, by William Watts (1752-1851), book illustrator and engraver of several Clwyd prints for John Boydell. This plate, after Thomas Sandby (1721-98), elder brother of Paul Sandby and a noted architectural draughtsman in his own right, is one of six by Watts utilised by Sir Richard Colt Hoare, the noted Wiltshire antiquary and amateur landscape painter, in his *Forty-Eight Views of the Seats of Noblemen & Gentlemen* (1795). In 1775 the Lleweni estate was purchased by the Hon. Thomas Fitzmaurice, who in 1780 erected there a linen bleachery, 'the most elegant structure of its kind in Europe', costing £20,000. He intended it primarily for the brown linens which his tenants in Ireland wove for him by way of rent (some 4,000 pieces a year), but weavers from adjacent parts of Denbighshire and Flintshire also brought their linen here. Following his death in 1793, the works was let to a Mr. Dumbell and then to J. Matthews & Co., who between 1800 and 1807 established depots at Chester, Caernarvon and Denbigh for collecting unbleached linen. In 1809, following bankruptcy proceedings, the Lleweni estate was sold and shortly afterwards the bleach works was demolished.

7. THE BRIDGE AT LLANRWST, DENBIGHSHIRE
An aquatint engraving, dated 1786, by Paul Sandby (1725-1809) after L. Nixon, an amateur etcher and draughtsman for other engravers. Sandby travelled widely in Britain, being one of the first to depict the beauties of Welsh scenery. His landscapes in gouache and water-colour have great charm. He was the first to practise aquatint engraving in England. Six plates of Clwyd views were included in his *Twelve Views of North Wales* (1776). Pont Fawr over the Conway links Llanrwst and Trewydir and was built *c.* 1636 of local slate and gritstone. The present approaches are less steep than as shown in early prints. The association of Inigo Jones with the bridge is no longer accepted.

8. WREXHAM PARISH CHURCH
A line engraving by Thomas Bradshaw, Jnr., of whom, unfortunately, little is known. In that the print is dedicated to William Robinson of Gwersyllt, M.P. for the Denbigh boroughs, it may be dated to 1705-8, and is the earliest, as well as the largest representation of the church. No alterations have been made to the exterior of the building since its virtual reconstruction in the early-sixteenth century, apart from minor repairs to the fabric carried out after the restoration of the episcopacy in 1660.

9. EASTERN VIEW OF WREXHAM CHURCH
A lithograph by J.W. Walton (*fl. c.* 1850) from an original drawing by Frederick Peake, printed by Day & Haghe, and published in 1843 by Thomas Painter, who carried on the business of bookseller and publisher in Wrexham from 1825 to 1855. Few parts of Wrexham have altered so much as this area. The view is taken looking along Mount Street, then known as 'The Green', towards the Green Steps leading down fom the church-yard. Many buildings have disappeared following brewery developments in 1854-79, and the building of the Wrexham & Ellesmere Railway in 1895.

10. RUTHIN TOWN HALL
A line engraving by W. Wallis after Henry Gastineau (1791-1876), a water-colour painter who exhibited at the Royal Academy and elsewhere from 1812 to 1875. Engravings of thirty-eight of his Denbighshire and Flintshire landscapes were published in *Wales Illustrated* (1830). The old Town Hall occupied the site of the car park in St. Peter's Square. It was built in 1663 using stone from the ruinous chancel of the church. For two hundred years the court of the town was held there. In 1785 the County Hall was built in Record Street, and shortly after Market Street was laid out (*c.* 1863) the present Town Hall and Market were erected. The old Town Hall ceased to have any practical function and was demolished in 1863.

11. MOLD HIGH STREET

This is one of a series of mid-Victorian scenes of Mold by Pring & Price. It shows the site of the Cross (with clock) and the Market Hall which was erected in 1849 by the Mold Market Company on the site of the former Leet Hall, a 'barn-like crazy old building', which had become so ruinous that when it rained, the judges would 'feel the rain dripping through the roof on to their heads as they sat on the bench'. The new hall, 'one of the largest of its kind in Wales', accommodated market stalls, chiefly for butchers, while the upper floor contained assembly rooms.

12. ST. WINEFRIDE'S WELL

This is an early line engraving. The Well and Chapel were built *c.* 1500 on the traditional site of the martyrdom of St. Winefride (seventh century), probably replacing an earlier medieval shrine. In eighteenth-century England the expansion of the print market not only encouraged new work based on artists' orginal sketches, but also prolonged the life of existing plates, even those 'bought for old copper'. This particular print is a case in point, at least five states of the plate being discernible, covering a period of some eighty years. Engraved by Francis Place (1647-1728) and published by P. Tempest (*c.* 1650-1717), it originally appeared in *The Life and Miracles of St. Winefride* (1713). The plate passed into the possession of Thomas Bakewell in Fleet Street, who published an edition in 1731, and later of John Bowles (*fl.* 1720-79), print and map seller, when, much reduced in size, with the disappearance of the legend of St. Winefride, it appears under the imprint 'John Bowles & Son', current 1753-64. After Bowles's death in 1779, his stock was taken over by Robert Wilkinson (*fl.* 1775-1829), and the print next appears (1779-84) under the latter's imprint. In its final stage the print appears under the imprint (current 1784-94) of Robert Sayer, map and print seller of Fleet Street, again reduced in size, as if indicating that the edges of the plate had been damaged.

13. NORTHOP CHURCH

Another lithograph by George Hawkins, printed by Day & Haghe. It is the only Clwyd print that actually shows a church in the process of restoration. The church of St. Eurgain and St. Peter, Northop, had been in a dilapidated condition during the eighteenth century, but it was not until 1837 that the vestry decided to carry out the necessary repairs. They accepted the proposals of Thomas Jones, the Chester architect, who was also responsible for designing Talacre Hall, the Deanery, St.Asaph, the County Hall, Mold, Bryn Asaph, and the extensions to Llanferres (1843) and Nercwys (1847) churches. The tower and roof were to be retained. Restoration therefore involved supporting the roof and rebuilding the walls of the nave and north aisle. This was achieved at a cost of £1,450, and services were resumed in the building on 6 October 1840.

14. HAWARDEN CASTLE AND PARK IN FLINTSHIRE

One of a series of large line engravings of country seats in North Wales made in 1740 by W.H. Toms (*c.* 1712-50) from original drawings by Thomas Badeslade (*fl.* 1719-50), draughtsman and surveyor, this print depicts the ruins of the stone castle built at Hawarden to replace that destroyed in 1282. It was dismantled in 1645 by order of Parliament. The mansion to the north-east is Broadlane Hall. The castle and manor of Hawarden were purchased by Sir John Glynne after the Civil War. The present castle dates from 1752 with additions in 1809. This is the particular print that inspired John Boydell to turn to engraving for a living. As Boydell himself wrote: 'It happened soon after that time that a large Print of Hawarden Castle and the Country adjacent drawn by Mr. Badeslade and Engraved by Wm. Harry Toms in London was just finished. I admired it to a great degree, finding it was an employment that many have got a livelihood by — I thought I should like to follow the art of Engraving. My friends enquired of Mr. Badeslade relating to my wishes, wrote to Mr. Toms who offered to take me on tryal'.

15. RHYL, NORTH WALES

A lithograph by Newman & Co., London, c. 1852, depicting, as Slater's *Directory* has it 'the watering place rapidly rising to that respectability and note which the great beauty of the site and salubrity of its air so justly entitle it'. The softening effect of the sea and hills, the wealth of detail in the fore- and middle-ground, the delicate effect of cloud, light and shadows — all helping to reduce the harsh outlines of the buildings — combine to produce a fine example of mid-nineteenth century lithography. The print is very accurate and can be correlated with a plan of the township of Rhyl, 1852, when the built-up area of Rhyl extended from Crescent Road to Sea Street (Church Street) and north of the Quay Street (Wellington Road) and Church Street (Russell Street), when the first public sewer had just been proposed and when marshes, crossed by 'public open drains', lay between the town and the packet station at Voryd.

16. PENLEY CHURCH

An aquatint by G. Hunt after David Cox (1783-1859), whose work was so intimately connected with Wales and the Welsh landscape. The drawing is a simple, even crude and superficial treatment of the subject, perhaps deliberately so since it appears in one of Cox's more conventional treatises on painting — *A Series of Progressive Lessons* (1823). The existence of the print, however, poses problems for local historians. The present church at Penley was built in 1900-1, replacing an earlier dilapidated church of 'debased Gothic' and 'Georgian Italian' style to which church records (very late in time, 1897) attribute a construction date of 1794. This print depicts its predecessor, 'the Old Church of Timber, lath & plaister', ostensibly, therefore, demolished about 1793, at which point in time David Cox was only ten years old. Either Cox's sketch for tutorial purposes is based on one by another, earlier artist, or else the *enlargement* of the '1794 church' to twice its former size, that later records assert took place in 1819 during the incumbency (1786-1823) of the Rev. John Cooper, actually refers to the building of a new church which was replaced in 1901.

17. FLINT CASTLE, NORTH WALES

Line engraving by J.H. Kernot (*fl.* 1830s) after J.M.W. Turner (1775-1851), who began as a water-colourist in a meticulous topographical style, and between 1798 and 1801 travelled extensively in Yorkshire, Scotland and Wales. He died a rich man, partly through the great demand in his time for engravings of picturesque scenery, for which he supplied originals. Clwyd landscapes were engraved by J.T. Willmore (1800-63), J.C. Varrall (*fl.* 1815-30) and J. Walker (*fl. c.* 1800), but none as successfully as Kernot, who captures on steel the many facets of Turner's work.

18. HALKYN CASTLE, FLINTSHIRE

A lithograph by William Westall (1781-1850), engraver and publisher, after J. Chessel Buckler (1770-1851), and printed by C. Hullmandel (1781-1850), an important pioneer figure in lithographic engraving and printing. The mineral rights over a large part of Halkyn Mountain were vested in the Grosvenor family, and in 1824 Earl Grosvenor erected near Catch ' a splendid castellated mansion in the ancient English style of architecture, commanding some of the finest views for which the strikingly diversified scenery of the neighbourhood is celebrated; this seat, called Halkin Castle, is occasionally the residence of that nobleman's family'.

19. THE LIGHTHOUSE ON POINT OF AIR

An aquatint drawn and engraved by William Daniell (1769-1837) in 1815 and published in his *Voyage Round Great Britain*, the record of a voyage made in 1813, starting at Land's End. Of the twenty-five prints depicting scenes along the coast of Wales, this is the only one of the Clwyd coastline. The lighthouse was built in 1777 by a trust comprising the mayor, recorder and aldermen of Chester. About 1823-5, by then taken over by Trinity House, it was partly rebuilt. In 1844 it was replaced by a new iron lighthouse further out to sea, and in about 1865 by the *Dee* lightship. It is now disused.

20. **OVERTON BRIDGE**

An aquatint engraving by Francis Jukes (1745-1812), noted for his landscapes and sporting scenes, after an original painting by Thomas Walmsley (1763-1805), a landscape artist who exhibited at the Royal Academy. The bridge is probably that 'repaired' or rebuilt in 1666 and is the immediate predecessor of the present structure begun in 1814 some fifty yards downstream of the old bridge.

21. **CORWEN**

The firm of Newman & Co. was amongst the most prolific engravers of North Wales scenes, and this print of Corwen in the Edeyrnion district of Merioneth, now in the county of Clwyd, is typical of their work. Their workmanlike and competent prints were often published by local shopkeepers and printers, and appeared in a variety of guide books (and illustrated books) throughout the nineteenth century.

22. **CYNWYD MILL**

A lithograph by J. Townshend, printed and published by C. Hullmandel, 1824. Cynwyd is a small village midway between Corwen and Llandrillo. It lies at the mouth of the valley of the Afon Trystion, which runs up between hills whose slopes are now clothed by the Cynwyd Forest. Many tourists and artists — Edward Pugh, Hugh Hughes, Rev. W. Bingley, Paul Sandby and Thomas Walmsley — are on record as having left the main highway to make their way 'through a labyrinth of young wood of almost impenetrable thickness' to visit the waterfall, Rhaeadr Cynwyd. Pugh mentions many points in this valley as being 'irresistible to a draughtsman', particularly the old mill which was 'an object of much consequence, as from its age and figure it increases the rustic effect of this hollow'.

23. **JOHN BOYDELL (1719-1804)**

Line engraving by H. Meyer from an original picture by G. Stuart, 1814.

24. **MOSES GRIFFITH (1747-1819)**

A self-portrait, now in the National Library of Wales, painted in 1811.

The County Archivist is grateful to the National Museum of Wales for permission to reproduce the etching 'The Artist travelling in Wales', by T. Rowlandson (cover), and to the National Library of Wales for the following prints — Nos. 2, 4, 7, 9, 16, 20, 21, 22 & 24.

DENBIGH CASTLE
Line engraving by J. Boydell, 1750

1.

BOW MEETING AT ERDDIG
Aquatint by W.J. Bennett after J. Townshend, 1823

2.

VALLE CRUCIS ABBEY

Line engraving by S. & N. Buck, 1742

3.

CHIRK VIADUCT
Lithograph by G. Hawkins, c. 1850

4.

LLANGOLLEN
Lithograph by G. Hawkins

5.

LLEWENI BLEACH WORKS
Line engraving by W. Watts after T. Sandby, 1792

6.

LLANRWST BRIDGE
Aquatint by Paul Sandby after L. Nixon, 1786

7.

WREXHAM CHURCH

Line engraving by Thomas Bradshaw, junior, c. 1707

8.

EASTERN VIEW OF WREXHAM CHURCH
Lithograph by J.W. Walton, 1843

9.

RUTHIN TOWN HALL

Line engraving by W. Wallis after H. Gastineau, 1830

10.

MOLD HIGH STREET
Lithograph published by Pring & Price

11.

ST. WINEFRIDE'S WELL
Line engraving by Francis Place, originally published in 1713

12.

NORTHOP CHURCH
Lithograph by G. Hawkins, 1839

13.

HAWARDEN CASTLE
Line engraving by W.H. Toms after T. Badeslade, 1740

14.

RHYL
Lithograph by Newman & Co., c. 1852

15.

PENLEY CHURCH
Aquatint by G. Hunt after D. Cox, 1823

16.

FLINT CASTLE

Line engraving by J.H. Kernot after J.M.W. Turner, 1836

17.

HALKYN CASTLE
Lithograph by W. Westall after J.C. Buckler, 1826

18.

POINT OF AYR LIGHTHOUSE
Aquatint by William Daniell, 1815

19.

OVERTON BRIDGE

Aquatint by F. Jukes after T. Walmsley, 1794

20.

CORWEN
Line engraving by Newman & Co.

21.

CYNWYD MILL
Lithograph by J. Townshend, 1824

22.

JOHN BOYDELL (1719-1804)   *23.*

24.   *MOSES GRIFFITH (1747-1819)*

THE TOPOGRAPHICAL PRINTS OF CLWYD

DENBIGHSHIRE

1. ABERGELE CHURCH, Denbighshire. 65 x 90. Line engraving by Rock & Co., London, 14 September 1857.

2. ABERGELEY. Market Street. 55 x 80. Line engraving. Published by R. Jones, printer, etc., Abergeley.

3. ACREFAIR, Near Wynnstay on the River Dee. 301 x 424. Aquatint by F. Jukes after T. Walmsley. Dedicated to the Right Honble Lord Viscount Bulkeley. Published by F. Jukes, 10 Howland St., 10 January 1794. Also in T. Walmsley & F. Jukes, *Views in North Wales,* 1792-4.

4. ACTON HALL, Denbighshire. 84 x 121. Line engraving by T. Barber after J.P. Neale, June 1829. Published by J.P. Neale, 16 Bennet St., Blackfriars Road. Also in J.P. Neale, *Views of the Seats of Noblemen,* 1824-9.

5. ACTON PARK. 148 x 224. Lithograph by Henry Grueber. Printed by Engelmann, Graf, Coindet & Co. Published in H. Grueber, *Six Lithographic Views of Seats in the Neighbourhood of Wrexham, North Wales.*
    CRO

6. ACTON PARK in Denbighshire, the Seat of Sir Foster Cunliffe, Bart. 96 x 150. Line engraving by [W.] Thomas after [W.] Evans. Published by Harrison & Co., 18 Paternoster Row, London, 1 July 1788. Also in *Picturesque Views of the Principal Seats of the Nobility,* 1787-8.
    CRO

7. BATHAFERN HILLS from Coedmarchan Rocks. 223 x 300. Aquatint by W. Ellis after E. Pugh. Dedicated to the Rt. Hon. Lord William Beauclerk. Published by E. Pugh, Great Queen Street, Lincoln's Inn Fields, 24 November 1794.

8. BOD-NOD [BODNANT], Denbighshire, The Seat of William Hanmer, Esqr. 163 x 245. Lithograph. Drawn and printed by C.J. Greenwood.
    CRO

9. BROUGHTON HALL. 154 x 231. Line engraving by S. Middiman, *c.* 1805.

10. BROUGHTON HALL. 176 x 254. Line engraving by J. Basire after W.D. Fryer. Published by J. Hatchard, Piccadilly, 1 January 1805.

11. BRYMBO HALL, Denbighshire. The Property of John Wilkinson, Esq. 255 x 360. Lithograph [? by W.R. Dickinson], *c.* 1835.

12. BRYNKINALLT, Denbighshire. The Seat of Viscount Dungannon. 125 x 196. Line engraving. Published by W. Price, Oswestry.

13. BRYNKINALLT, Denbighshire. The Seat of Viscount Dungannon, MP. 207 x 300. Lithograph by W.L. Leitch after Ross. Printed by Day & Haghe. Published by W. Price, Bookseller, Oswestry.

14. BRYNKINALT, Denbighshire. The Seat of the Rt. Honble the Viscount Dungannon. 162 x 247. Lithograph. Drawn and printed by C.J. Greenwood.

15. CAPEL GARMON, Carnedd enclosing a cromlech at. 67 x 95. Woodcut. [Vignette].

16. CHIRK AQUEDUCT, Denbighshire. 289 x 450. Aquatint/etching by C. Jackson after C.A. Hulbert. Published by C. Hulbert, Shrewsbury, 1827.

17. CHIRK AQUEDUCT, Denbighshire. 185 x 253. Lithograph by C. Hullmandel. Published by T. Catherall, Chester. Also in W.Cathrall, *History of North Wales,* 1828.
CL

18. CHIRK AQUEDUCT, Denbighshire. 90 x 146. Line engraving by T. Barber after H. Gastineau. Published by Jones & Co., Temple of the Muses, Finsbury Square, London. Also in *Wales Illustrated,* 1830.
CRO

19. CHIRK AQUEDUCT, Denbighshire. 71 x 120. Line engraving by S. Lacey.

20. CHIRK AQUEDUCT, North Wales. 133 x 195. Lithograph by G.Pickering. Published by J.Seacome, Bookseller, Chester. Printed by Engelmann & Co. Also in G.Pickering, *Four Picturesque Views in North Wales.*
CRO

21. CHIRCK CASTLE in the County of Denbigh, The North View of. 145 x 352. Line engraving by S. and N. Buck. Published in S. and N. Buck, *Views of all the Castles,* 1742.
CRO

22. CHIRCK CASTLE in the County of Denbigh, The North View of. 73 x 138. Line engraving. Published in *A Description of England and Wales,* 1769.
CRO

23. CHIRCK CASTLE in Denbighshire, View of. 150 x 226. Line engraving. Published in *England Display'd,* 1769.

24. CHIRCK CASTLE in Denbighshire, View of. 124 x 204. Line engraving. Published in the *British Magazine,* April 1772.
CRO

25. CHIRK CASTLE. 272 x 179. Line engraving by P.Mazell after M.Griffith. Published in T. Pennant, *A Tour in Wales,* 1778.
CRO*

26. CHIRK CASTLE in Denbighshire, the Seat of Richard Myddelton, Esq. 97 x 158. Line engraving by Walker after Evans. Published by H.D. Symonds, No. 20 & Allen & West No. 15 Paternoster Row & T. Conder, Bucklersbury, London, 16 April 1798.

27. CHIRK CASTLE. 165 x 278. Aquatint by T.H. Fielding after T. Girtin. Published by T. Clay, 18 Ludgate Hill, London, 1 May 1820. Also in T. Compton, *The Northern Cambrian Mountains,* 1820.

28. CHIRK CASTLE. 43 x 71. Line engraving. Published in T. Evans, *Walks through Wales,* 1819, and G.A. Cooke, *Topographical and Statistical Description of North Wales, c.* 1830.
CL

29. CHIRK CASTLE. 41 x 67. Line engraving. Published by T.T. & J. Tegg, Cheapside, 1 October 1832. Also in G.N. Wright, *Scenes in North Wales,* 1833.
CRO*

30. CHIRK CASTLE. 188 x 129. Etching. Drawn and etched by A. Clint. Published by H. Colburn, 13 Great Marlborough St. Also in G.J. Bennett, *A Pedestrian Tour Through North Wales,* 1838.
CRO*

31. CHIRK CASTLE. 118 x 178. Photo-lithograph after E.H. Lloyd, 1881.

32. CHIRK CASTLE. 96 x 143. Lithograph by W. Crane, [Chester].
CRO

33. CHIRK CASTLE, Denbighshire. 102 x 153. Line engraving by Stewart after J.P. Neale. Published by John Harris, St. Paul's Church Yard, 1 June 1813. Also in J. Evans, *The Beauties of England and Wales*, 1812.
CRO

34. CHIRK CASTLE, Denbighshire. 87 x 125. Line engraving by H. Bond after J.P. Neale. Published by J.P. Neale, 16 Bennet St., Blackfriars' Road, 1 November 1828. Also in J.P. Neale, *Views of the Seats of Noblemen*, 1824-9.
CRO

35. CHIRK CASTLE, Denbighshire. 82 x 131. Line engraving by J. Horsburgh after R.K. Penson.

36. CHIRK CASTLE, Denbighshire. 90 x 143. Line engraving by J.C. Varrall after H. Gastineau. Published in *Wales Illustrated*, 1830.
CRO

37. CHIRK CASTLE, Denbighshire. 115 x 154. Line engraving by J. Newman, 48 Watling St. Published by H. Jones, Llangollen.
CRO

38. CHIRK CASTLE, Denbighshire, Seat of R. Myddleton, Esquire. 28 x 64. Line engraving, February 1799.

39. CHIRK CASTLE in Denbighshire, The North-East Prospect of. One of the Seats of John Myddelton, Esqr. 395 x 616. Line engraving by W.H. Toms after T. Badeslade. Published 17 October 1735.

40. CHIRK CASTLE in Denbighshire, The West Prospect of. One of the Seats of John Myddelton, Esqr. 418 x 706. Line engraving by W.H. Toms after T. Badeslade, *c.* 1735.

41. CHIRKE CASTLE in Denbighshire, the Seat of Richard Myddelton Esq. 104 x 160. Line engraving by Walker after Evans. Published by Harrison & Co., 18 Paternoster Row, 1 May 1788. Published in *Picturesque Views of the Principal Seats of the Nobility*, 1787-8.

42. CHIRK CASTLE. North View. 82 x 175. Photo-lithograph after E.H. Lloyd, 1881.

43. CHIRK CASTLE, North East View of. 101 x 175. Photo-lithograph after E.H. Lloyd. Drawn and printed at the London Drawing Office, 1884.

44. CHIRK CASTLE, South View of. 100 x 173. Photo-lithograph after E.H. Lloyd. Drawn and printed at the London Drawing Office, 1884.

45. CHIRK CASTLE ... from Wynnstay Park. 205 x 288. Aquatint by P. Sandby. Published by P. Sandby, St. Georges Row, 1 September 1776. Also in P. Sandby, *Twelve Views in North Wales*, 1776.

46. CHIRK VIADUCT - Shrewsbury and Chester Railway. Length 846 feet, Height 100 feet, Number of Arches 12, Span of 10 Stone Arches 45 feet, Span of 2 Timber Arches 120 feet. Henry Robertson, Engineer. 187 x 276. Lithograph by G. Hawkins after G. Pickering. Day & Son, Lithographers. Published by T. Catherall, Eastgate Row, Chester, *c.* 1851.

47. CLWYD, VALE OF, from Denbigh Castle. 81 x 304. Chromo-gravure.

48. CLYDD, VALE OF. 122 x 187. Aquatint. Published by [Thomas] McLean, Haymarket, London, 1822. Also in T. McLean, *A Picturesque Description of North Wales*, 1823.

49. COLWYN BAY. 80 x 110. Line engraving by Newman & Co., 28 February 1877. Published in *Seventy-two Views of North Wales*.

50. [COLWYN BAY]. Colwyn Bay Hotel. 80 x 108. Line engraving by Newman & Co. February 1877. Published in *Seventy-two Views of North Wales*.

51. [COLWYN BAY]. Colwyn Bay Hotel. 80 x 105. Line engraving by Newman & Co. 20 August 1878.

52. [COLWYN BAY]. Conway Road. 80 x 110. Line engraving by Newman & Co. 28 February 1877. Published in *Seventy-two Views of North Wales*.

53. COLWYN BAY. Llandrillo Church. 80 x 110. Line engraving by Newman & Co. 28 February 1877. Published in *Seventy-two Views of North Wales*.

54. [COLWYN BAY]. Pwllycrochon Hotel. 80 x 110. Line engraving by Newman & Co. February 1877. Published in *Seventy-two Views of North Wales*.

55. [COLWYN BAY]. Pwllycrochon Hotel No. 2. 85 x 110. Line engraving by Newman & Co. 23 August 1878. Published in *Seventy-two Views of North Wales*.

56. DEE, A Scene on the. 316 x 240. Lithograph [by C. Marsh] after T[homas] B[arker]. Published in T. Barker, *Thirty-two Lithographic Impressions of Landscape Scenery*, 1814.

57. DEE VIADUCT. Shrewsbury & Chester Railway. Length 1508 Feet, Height 147 Feet, 19 Arches. 105 x 160. Line engraving by Newman & Co., 48 Watling Street. Published by R. Hughes & Son, Church Street, Wrexham.
CRO

58. DENBIGH. 150 x 450. Soft ground etching by J.G. Wood. Published in J.G. Wood, *The Principal Rivers of Wales*, 1813.

59. DENBIGH. 250 x 390. Lithograph by C. Hullmandel after F. N[icholson?]. 1822.
CRO

60. DENBIGH. 62 x 92. Line engraving by Edward Finden after Capt. Robert Batty. Published by John Murray, London, 1 August 1823. Also in R. Batty, *Welsh Scenery*, 1823.
CL

61. DENBIGH. 93 x 149. Line engraving by W. Radclyffe after H. Gastineau. Published in *Wales Illustrated*, 1830.
CRO

62. DENBIGH. 41 x 67. Line engraving. Published by T.T. & J. Tegg, Cheapside, 1 October 1832. Also in G.N. Wright, *Scenes in North Wales*, 1833.
CRO*

63. DENBIGH. 90 x 155. Line engraving by J. Harwood, 26 Fenchurch Street, London. No. 729. 24 August 1847. Published in J. Williams, *Ancient and Modern Denbigh*, 1856.
CRO

64. DENBIGH, The Burgess Tower. 237 x 274. Photo-lithograph after Lloyd-Williams and Underwood. Printed by A. Macgregor, Liverpool and Manchester. Published in Lloyd-Williams & Underwood, *Village Churches of Denbighshire*, 1872.
CRO*

65. DENBIGH, The Capital Town of the County. 338 x 786. Line engraving by I. Lewis. Dedicated to the Hon. Sir Robert Salusbury Cotton of Lleweny, Bart.

66. DENBIGH, Near. [End view of primitive water mill] . 105 x 145. Lithograph.

67. DENBIGH, The New Church. Thomas Penson Architect. 205 x 202. Lithograph by T.M. Penson, printed by Day & Haghe.

68. DENBIGH, The North-East View of the Hospital for the Treatment of the Insane at. 255 x 454. Lithograph by G. Hawkins. Printed by Day & Haghe. Dedicated to Joseph Ablett of Llanbedr Hall by Thomas Fulljames, FRIBA, Architect & County Surveyor of Gloucester, *c*. 1850.

69. DENBIGH, North Wales. 230 x 325. Lithograph by Newman & Co. Published by Thomas Gee, Denbigh.

70. DENBIGH, North Wales Hospital for the Insane. 72 x 110. Line engraving. Published by Thos. Gee, Denbigh. Also in J. Williams, *Ancient and Modern Denbigh*, 1856.
CRO*

71. DENBIGH, St. Marcellus or Whitchurch. 96 x 156. Line engraving by J. Newman & Co., 48 Watling Street, London, published by J. Williams, Vale St., Denbigh. Also in J. Williams, *Ancient and Modern Denbigh*, 1856.
CRO*

72. DENBIGH, From the Stone Quarries. 90 x 155. Lithograph by R. Anderson after W. Simpson from a photograph by Bedford. Published by Blackie & Son, London, Glasgow and Edinburgh. Also in O. Jones, *Cymru: Yn Hanesyddol, Parthedegol a Bywgraphyddol*, cyf. 1, 1875.
CL

73. DENBIGH, The Town of. 103 x 152. Line engraving by J. & H.S. Storer after G. Pickering. Published in W. Cathrall, *History of North Wales*, 1828.
CL

74. DENBIGH ABBY, The North East View of. 148 x 360. Line engraving by S. and N. Buck, 9 April 1742. Published in S. and N. Buck, *Views of all the Castles*, 1742.
CRO

75. DENBIGH CASTLE, Denbeighshire. 114 x 160. Line engraving by [S.] Sparrow. Published by S. Hooper, 7 August 1786. Also in F. Grose, *The Antiquities of England and Wales*, 1786.
CRO

76. DENBIGH CASTLE. 82 x 130. Line engraving by J. Ryland [after B. Ralph] . Published in *England Illustrated*, 1764.

77. DENBIGH CASTLE. 178 x 132. Line engraving after M. Griffith. Published in T. Pennant, *A Tour in Wales*, 1784.
CRO*

78. DENBIGH CASTLE. 87 x 130. Line engraving by J. Ryland.

79. DENBIGH CASTLE. 155 x 226. Aquatint by T. Fielding after F. Nicholson. Published by T. Clay, 18 Ludgate Hill, London, 1 May 1820, and in T. Compton, *The Northern Cambrian Mountains*, 1820.

80. DENBIGH CASTLE. 41 x 67. Line engraving. Published by T.T. & J. Tegg, Cheapside, 1 October 1832. Also in G.N. Wright, *Scenes in North Wales*, 1833.
CRO*

81. DENBIGH CASTLE. 70 x 112. Line engraving. Published by Thos. Gee, Denbigh. Also in J. Williams, *Ancient and Modern Denbigh*, 1856.
CRO*

82. DENBIGH CASTLE. 104 x 152 rounded. Aquatint by [J.] Ross after M. Griffith.

83. [DENBIGH CASTLE]. 104 x 169. Aquatint.

84. DENBIGH CASTLE. 82 x 130. Line engraving by Metcalf.
CRO

85. DENBIGH CASTLE. 72 x 100. Line engraving by Newman & Co.

86. DENBIGH CASTLE. (Castell Dinbych). 72 x 100. Line engraving by Newman & Co. Published in W. Davis, *Hand-Book for the Vale of Clwyd*, 1856.
CRO

87. DENBIGH CASTLE. (Castell Dinbych). 195 x 280. Lithograph by Newman & Co., 48 Watling St., London.

88. DENBIGH CASTLE. (Castell Dinbych). 194 x 280. Lithograph by Newman & Co., 48 Watling St., London. Sold by D.Ll. Lewes, Rhyl.
CRO

89. DENBIGH CASTLE. (Castell Dinbych). 225 x 318. Lithograph by Newman & Co. Published by Thomas Gee, Denbigh.

90. DENBIGH CASTLE, Denbighshire. 86 x 60. Line engraving by J. Storer after E. Dayes. Published by W. Corke, New Bond Street, and J. Carpenter, Old Bond Street, 1 April 1808. Also in J.S. Storer & J. Greig, *Antiquarian and Topographical Cabinet*, 1807-11.

91. DENBIGH CASTLE, Denbighshire. 93 x 149. Line engraving by W. Radclyffe after H. Gastineau. Published in *Wales Illustrated*, 1830.
CRO

92. DENBIGH CASTLE in Denbighshire. 135 x 182. Line engraving by Thornton. Published by Alexander Hogg, 16 Paternoster Row, London, *c.* 1790.
CRO

93. DENBIGH CASTLE. Gateway. 237 x 255. Photo-lithograph after Lloyd-Williams & Underwood. Printed by A. Macgregor (late Maclure, Macdonald and Macgregor), Liverpool & Manchester, 1872.
CRO

94. DENBIGH CASTLE, Gateway at. 225 x 304. Etching by George Cuitt, 1813. Published in G. Cuitt, *Etchings of Ancient Buildings*, 1816, and *Wanderings and Pencillings*, 1855.
CRO*

95. DENBIGH CASTLE, Gateway of. 63 x 91. Line engraving by Edward Finden after Capt. R[obert] Batty. Published by John Murray, London, 1 May 1823. Also in R. Batty, *Welsh Scenery*, 1823.
CL

96. DENBIGH CASTLE. Great Gateway. 130 x 230. Etching.
CRO

97. DENBIGH CASTLE, The North East View of. 145 x 350. Line engraving by S. and N. Buck, 9 April 1742. Published in S. and N. Buck, *Views of all the Castles,* 1742. CRO

98. DENBIGH CASTLE, The North East View of. 73 x 138. Line engraving. Published in *A Description of England and Wales,* 1769. CRO

99. DENBIGH CASTLE. North View. 94 x 175. Photo-lithograph [after E.H. Lloyd], 1881.

100. DENBIGH CASTLE, The North View of. 149 x 352. Line engraving by S. and N. Buck, 9 April 1742. Published in S. and N. Buck, *Views of all the Castles,* 1742. CRO

101. DENBIGH CASTLE, North Wales. 180 x 250. Etching by Letitia Byrne after F. Nicholson. Published by Thomas Palser, Surry Side, Westminster Bridge, 2 January 1809.

102. DENBIGH CASTLE, North Wales. 98 x 152. Line engraving by T. Owen after J.P. Neale. Published by John Harris, St. Paul's Churchyard, London, 1 July 1814. Also in J. Evans, *The Beauties of England and Wales,* 1812. CRO

103. DENBIGH CASTLE in North Wales, A North View of. 280 x 432. Line engraving. Drawn, engraved and published by J. Boydell, at the Globe near Durham Yard in the Strand, 1750. CRO

104. DENBIGH CASTLE AND TOWN. 72 x 92. Line engraving by Newman & Co., 48 Watling Street, for D.Ll. Lewis, Rhyl.

105. DENBIGH HIGH CROSS. 148 x 80. Lithograph by Woodall, Minshall, Oswestry, *c.* 1886.

106. DERWEN CHURCH AND CROSS. 168 x 122. Line engraving. Published in E. Owen, *Old Stone Crosses of the Vale of Clwyd,* 1886. CRO*

107. DINAS BRAN. 114 x 193. Photo-lithograph [after E.H. Lloyd], 1881.

108. DINAS BRAN. 75 x 90. Line engraving. In extra-illustrated volume (N.L.W.) of *Roadside Rigmarola, Rhymes Recording Rambles in North Wales,* 1861-4.

109. DINAS BRAN, Llangollen. 90 x 135. Lithograph. CRO

110. DINAS BRAN. South East View. 81 x 175. Photo-lithograph [after E.H. Lloyd], 1881.

111. DINAS BRAN CASTLE. 161 x 208 diam. Line engraving by J. Basire, 20 August 1785.

112. DINAS BRÂN CASTLE in the County of Denbigh, The South East View of. 148 x 351. Line engraving by S. and N. Buck. Published in S. and N. Buck, *Views of all the Castles,* 1742. CRO

113. DINAS BRAN CASTLE in the County of Denbigh, View of. 157 x 268. Line engraving. Published in the *Modern Universal British Traveller,* 1779.
CRO

114. DINAS BRAN CASTLE, Denbighshire. 60 x 74. Line engraving. Published in *An Account of the Principal Pleasure Tours in England and Wales,* 1822.

115. DINAS BRANE CASTLE from Llan Gollin. 207 x 281. Aquatint by Paul Sandby after Pilkington, 1784.

116. DINAS BRAN CASTLE near Llangollen. 331 x 298. Soft ground etching by Webber.

117. DINAS BRAN & LLANGOLLEN, Denbighshire. 65 x 94. Line engraving by Rock & Co.,10 March 1869. Published in Rock & Co., *Picturesque Views in North Wales.*

118. CASTEL DINAS BRÂN. 102 x 154. Lithograph by T.M. Baynes. Printed by C. Hullmandel. Published in G.J. Freeman, *Sketches in Wales,* 1826.
CL

119. CASTEL DINAS BRAN, Llangollen, Denbighshire. 60 x 90. Line engraving by Rock & Co. Published 15 February 1869.

120. CASTELL DINAS BRAN, Denbighshire, Remains of. 94 x 148. Line engraving by W. Wallis after H. Gastineau. Published in *Wales Illustrated,* 1830.
CRO

121. CASTELL DINAS BRAN from the South West. 100 x 174. Photo-lithograph. Drawn and printed at the London Drawing Office, 1884.

122. CASTLE DDINAS BRAN, Vale of Llangollen. 85 x 121.   Line engraving by William Miller after Montague Stanley. Published in A. & C. Black, *Picturesque Guide through North and South Wales,* 1851.
CL

123. CASTLE DINAS BRAN. 67 x 111. Etching by A. Clint. Published by H. Colburn, 13 Great Marlborough St. Also in G.J. Bennett, *A Pedestrian Tour Through North Wales,* 1838.
CRO*

124. CASTLE DINAS BRAN. 80 x 93. Line engraving by Newman & Co. Published by David Roberts, Llangollen, *c.* 1860.

125. CASTLE DINAS BRAN, Denbighshire. 70 x 80. Line engraving by Newman & Co. Published by David Roberts, Llangollen.

126. CASTLE DINAS BRAN, Denbighshire. 120 x 146. Line engraving by J. Newman, 48 Watling St. Published by H. Jones, Llangollen.
CRO

127. CASTLE DINAS BRAND in the Vale of Llangothlin. 391 x 563. Aquatint by B. Comte after [J.] Laporte.

128. CASTLE DINAS Y BRAAN. 166 x 157 diam. Etching by W.M. Craig, 1806.

129. CASTLE DYNAS BRAN. 180 x 276. Line engraving by W. Watts after M. Griffith. Published in T. Pennant, *A Tour in Wales,* 1778.
CRO*

130. DUFFRYN-ALLED in Denbighshire. The Seat of Philip York, Esqr. 128 x 186. Line engraving by W. Angus after John Bird. Published by W. Angus, 4 Gwynne's Buildings, Islington, 1 September 1797.
CRO

131. DYFFRYN ALLED, The Seat of Philip York, Esq., Denbighshire. 124 x 181. Line engraving by W. Watts after M. Griffith. Published by J. & J. Boydell, Cheapside, & at the Shakspeare Gallery, Pall Mall, 25 June 1792. Also in R.C. Hoare, *Forty-Eight Views of Noblemen's and Gentlemen's Seats*, 1795.
CRO

132. ERBISTOCK CHURCH. 306 x 429. Aquatint by F. Jukes after T. Walmsley. Dedicated to Rev. Mr. Strong. Published by F. Jukes, 10 Howland St., 31 May 1794. Also in T. Walmsley & F. Jukes, *Views in North Wales*, 1792-4.

133. ERBISTOCK CHURCH. 306 x 429. Etching and stipple engraving after T. Walmsley. Dedicated to Rev. Mr. Strong. Published by F. Jukes, 10 Howland Street, 31 May 1794.

134. ERBISTOCK MILL. 306 x 428. Aquatint by F. Jukes after T. Walmsley. Dedicated to the Rt. Honble Lord and Lady Dacre. Published by F. Jukes, 10 Howland Street, 12 June 1794. Also in T. Walmsley & F. Jukes, *Views in North Wales*, 1792-4.
CRO

135. ERDDIG. The Meeting of the Royal British Bowmen in the Grounds of Erthig, Denbighshire, the Seat of Simon Yorke, Esqr. on 13 September 1822. 206 x 300. Aquatint by [W.J.] Bennett after J. Townshend, 1823.

136. ERTHIG, Denbighshire. 106 x 158. Line engraving by [T.] Medland after Evans. Published by Harrison & Co., 18 Paternoster Row, London, 1 May 1792.
CRO

137. ERTHIG, Denbighshire. 116 x 158. Line engraving by [T.] Medland after Evans. Published by J. Walker, 16 Rosomans Street, London, 1 May 1792.
CRO

138. ERTHIG, Denbighshire. 85 x 124. Line engraving by J. Westley after J.P. Neale, 1828. Published by J.P. Neale, 16 Bennett Street, Blackfriars Road, 1 October 1828. Also in J.P. Neale, *Views of the Seats of Noblemen*, 1824-9.
CRO

139. ERTHIG in Denbighshire, The West Prospect of the Seat of Simon Yorke, Esq. 405 x 546. Line engraving by W.H. Toms after T. Badeslade, *c.* 1740.

140. ERTHIG in Denbighshire, the Seat of Philip Yorke, Esq. 108 x 160. Line engraving by [T.] Medland after Evans. Published by Harrison & Co., 18 Paternoster Row. Also in *Picturesque Views of the Principal Seats of the Nobility*, 1787-8.

141. EYARTH, View on the Clwyd near. 142 x 197. Aquatint by T. Cartwright after E. Pugh. Published by E. Williams, Strand, 15 June 1813. Also in E. Pugh, *Cambria Depicta*, 1816.
CRO*

142. EYARTH ROCKS. 140 x 194. Aquatint by J. Havell after E. Pugh. Published by E. Williams, Strand, 15 April 1814. Also in E. Pugh, *Cambria Depicta*, 1816.
CRO*

143. GARTHEWIN, Residence of Col. Wynne. 191 x 287. Lithograph by Richard Bowman. Printed by T. Physick, Manchester.

144. GLAN-Y-WERN, Denbighshire, The Seat of John Edward Madocks, Esqr. 164 x 255. Lithograph by C.J. Greenwood after J. Shaw.
CRO

145. GRESFORD. 124 x 295. Soft ground etching by J. Townshend, May 1822.

146. GRESFORD, The Vale of, near Wrexham. 64 x 89. Line engraving by Rock & Co., 16 January 1856.

147. GRESFORD CHURCH. 83 x 128. Wood engraving by Hugh Hughes. Published by J. Johnson, 1819. Also in H. Hughes, *The Beauties of Cambria*, 1823.
CRO*

148. GRESFORD CHURCH, near Wrexham. 60 x 89. Line engraving. Published by Rock & Co., 16 January 1856.

149. GRESFORD CHURCH, Tower. 337 x 250. Photo-lithograph after Lloyd-Williams and Underwood. Printed by A. Macgregor, Liverpool & Manchester. Published in Lloyd-Williams & Underwood, *Village Churches of Denbighshire*, 1872.
CRO*

150. GRESFORD COTTAGE, Denbighshire. 108 x 167. Line engraving by W. & J. Walker after T. Sanby, Junr. Published by J. Walker, 16 Rosomans Street, London, 1 March 1793.

151. GRESFORD COTTAGE, Denbighshire. 108 x 166. Line engraving by W. & J. Walker after T. Sanby, Jn. Published by Harrison & Co., 18 Paternoster Row, 1 March 1793. Also in *The Itinerant*, 1799.
CRO

152. GRESFORD VALE, Denbighshire. A View of the Shrewsbury and Chester Railway. 100 x 175. Line engraving by Newman & Co. Published by R. Hughes & Son, Wrexham, *c.* 1856.
CRO

153. GWAGNYNOG, Urn to Dr. Johnson at. 142 x 97. Line engraving by W. Thomas. Published by J. Sewell, 32 Cornhill, 1 January 1794. Also in *The European Magazine*.
CRO

154. GWERSYLLT PARK. 148 x 225. Lithograph by Henry Grueber. Printed by Engelmann, Graf, Coindet & Co., 14 Newman St., London. Published in H. Grueber, *Six Lithographic Views of Seats in the Neighbourhood of Wrexham, North Wales*.
CRO

155. GWERSYLLT PARK, Denbighshire, A Meeting of the Society of Royal British Archers in. 420 x 590. Aquatint by C.G. Apostool after R. Smirke and J. Emes. Dedicated to H.R.H. George, Prince of Wales. Published by J. Emes, 1 North Street, Upper Charlotte Street, 1 April 1794.

156. GWRYCH CASTLE. 65 x 90. Line engraving by Newman & Co., 48 Watling St., London. Published in W. Davis, *Hand-Book for the Vale of Clwyd*, 1856.
CRO*

157. GWRYCH CASTLE. 115 x 155. Line engraving by W. Banks & Son, Edinburgh. Published by T. Catherall, Chester. Also in T. Catherall, *Views in North Wales, c.* 1860.
CL

158.	GWRYCH CASTLE, Abergele. 95 x 140. Line engraving. Published by H. Humphreys, Castle Square, Caernarvon.

159.	GWRYCH CASTLE, near Abergele, Denbighshire. 65 x 92. Line engraving by Rock & Co., 7 June 1861.

160.	GWRYCH CASTLE, Denbighshire. 86 x 123. Line engraving by T. Jeavons after J.P. Neale, 1 February 1825. Published in J.P. Neale, *Views of the Seats of Noblemen*, 1824-9.

161.	GWRYCH CASTLE, The Seat of Lloyd Hesketh Bamford Hesketh, Esq. 175 x 253. Lithograph by G. Hawkins after G. Pickering. Published by T. Catherall, Chester. Printed by Day & Son.

162.	GWRYCH NEAR ABERGELE, Denbighshire, The Seat of B. Hesketh, Esq. 92 x 148. Line engraving by H. Adlard after H. Gastineau. Published in *Wales Illustrated*, 1830. CRO

163.	HENDRE HOUSE, Denbighshire, The Seat of Thomas Blackwall, Esq. 162 x 257. Lithograph by C.J. Greenwood after J. Shaw. CRO

164.	HOLT, Denbighshire. 88 x 145. Line engraving by T. Barber after H. Gastineau. Published in *Wales Illustrated*, 1830. CRO

165.	HOLT BRIDGE. 157 x 230. Soft ground etching by J.G. Wood. Published in J.G. Wood, *The Principal Rivers of Wales*, 1813.

166.	HOLT CASTLE. 236 x 160. Line engraving by Peter Mazell [after John Norden]. Published in T. Pennant, *A Tour in Wales*, 1778. CRO*

167.	HOLT CASTLE. 151 x 103. Line engraving. Published in the *London Magazine*, 1779.

168.	HOLT CASTLE. 264 x 176. Photo-lithograph. Drawn by E.H. Lloyd [after John Norden], 1881.

169.	[HOLT CASTLE]. 118 x 161. Photo-lithograph. Drawn by E.H. Lloyd [after Daniel King], 1881.

170.	HOLT CASTLE. 151 x 104. Line engraving.

171.	HOLT CASTLE in the County of Denbigh, The South View of. 149 x 352. Line engraving by S. and N. Buck. Published in S. and N. Buck, *Views of all the Castles*, 1742. CRO

172.	HOLT CASTLE, in the County of Denbigh, The South View of. 71 x 137. Line engraving. Published in *A Description of England and Wales*, 1769.

173.	HOLT CASTLE, South View of. 147 x 188. Line engraving by J. Basire, 1785.

174.	HOLT CASTLE in 1610. 239 x 159. Line engraving by P. Mazell. Published in T. Pennant, *Tours in Wales*, 1810.

175. KINMEL PARK, co. Denbigh, The Seat of H.R. Hughes, Esq. 115 x 195. Lithograph by W. Walton. Printed by Stannard & Dixon, 7 Poland St. Published in J.B. Burke, *A Visitation of the Seats and Arms of the Noblemen and Gentlemen of Great Britain*, 1854.
CRO

176. [LLANBEDR DYFFRYN CLWYD]. The Griffin Hotel. 160 x 215. Lithograph.

177. LLANBEDR HALL, Denbighshire, The Seat of Joseph Ablett, Esqr. 163 x 247. Lithograph by C.J. Greenwood after J. Shaw.

178. LLANBEDR HALL, near Ruthin, The Seat of John Jesse, Esq., FRS. 72 x 110. Line engraving by Newman & Co. Published by J. Clarke, Ruthin. Also in W. Davis, *Hand-Book for the Vale of Clwyd*, 1856.
CRO*

179. [LLANDRILLO-YN-RHOS]. BRYN EURYN, LLANDRILLO CHURCH, etc. 83 x 128. Wood engraving by H. Hughes. Published in H. Hughes, *The Beauties of Cambria*, 1823.
CRO*

180. LLANDRILLO-YN-RHOS CHURCH, Denbighshire, As restored 1856. 80 x 102. Line engraving by John H. Le Keux after H. Kennedy.

181. LLANDULAS CHURCH [Interior]. 108 x 127. Photo-lithograph by Whiteman & Bass, London. Published in D.R. Thomas, *History of the Diocese of St. Asaph*, 1874.
CRO

182. LLANERK, the Seat of Daniel Leo, Esq., Denbighshire. 129 x 182. Line engraving by [W.C.] Wilson after [Moses] Griffith. Published by J. & J. Boydell, 90 Cheapside & at the Shakspeare Gallery, Pall Mall, 25 March 1795. Also in R.C. Hoare, *Forty-Eight Views of Noblemen's and Gentlemen's Seats*, 1795.
CRO

183. LLANFWROG, RUTHIN and LLANBEDR. 225 x 302. Aquatint by W. Ellis after E. Pugh. Dedicated to the Rt. Hon. Lord Bagot. Published by E. Pugh, 13 Bedford St., Covent Garden, July 1794.

184. IN LLANGOLLAN. 275 x 218. Lithograph [by W. Robert Dickenson], *c.* 1835.

185. LLANGOLLEN. 125 x 189. Aquatint by S. Alken after J. Smith. Published in W. Sotheby & J. Smith, *A Tour through Parts of Wales*, 1794.

186. LLANGOLLEN. 109 x 167. Line engraving by J. Widnell after [E.] Dayes. Published by J. Walker, 16 Rosomans St., London, 1 January 1796. Also in *The Itinerant* (pl.96), 1799.
CRO

187. LANGOLLEN. 111 x 189. Aquatint by I. Hill [after T. Rowlandson]. Published by W. Wigstead, No. 40 Charing Cross, London, 7 September 1799. Also in H. Wigstead, *Tour to North and South Wales*, 1800.

188. LLANGOLLEN. 157 x 230. Soft ground etching by J.G. Wood. Published in J.G. Wood, *The Principal Rivers of Wales*, 1813.

189. LLANGOLLEN. 145 x 199. Aquatint by T. Cartwright after E. Pugh. Published by E. Williams, Strand, 15 January 1815. Also in E. Pugh, *Cambria Depicta*, 1816.
CRO*

190. LLANGOLLEN. 145 x 199. Aquatint by Thos. Cartwright after Edwd. Pugh. Published by E. Williams, Strand, 15 April 1813. Also in E. Pugh, *Cambria Depicta*, 1816.
CRO*

191. LLANGOLLEN. 157 x 243. Aquatint by D. Havell after T. Compton. Published by T. Clay, 18 Ludgate Hill, 2 March 1818. Also in T. Compton, *The Northern Cambrian Mountains*, 1820.
CRO

192. LLANGOLLEN. 62 x 91. Line engraving by Edward Finden after Capt. Robert Batty. Published by John Murray, London, 1 January 1823. Also in R. Batty, *Welsh Scenery*, 1823.
CL

193. LLANGOLLEN. 176 x 251. Etching [? by C.A. Hulbert, *c.* 1827].

194. LLANGOLLEN. 83 x 122. Etching. Drawn and etched by A. Clint. Published by H. Colburn, 13 Gt. Marlborough St. Also in G.J. Bennett, *A Pedestrian Tour Through North Wales*, 1838.
CRO*

195. LLANGOLLEN. 171 x 234. Lithograph by W. Frank, Bristol, *c.* 1840.

196. LLANGOLLEN. 100 x 155. Line engraving. Published by J. Harwood, 26 Fenchurch Street, London, 23 July 1846.

197. LLANGOLLEN. 105 x 162. Lithograph by W. Crane, Chester, *c.* 1850.

198. LLANGOLLEN. 57 x 90. Line engraving by Rock & Co., London, 15 March 1869. Published in *The Queen's Album of North Wales*.

199. LLANGOLLEN. 100 x 160. Line engraving. Published by T. Catherall, Chester. Also in T. Catherall, *Views in North Wales*, *c.* 1860.
CRO

200. LLANGOLLEN, Birch Tree. 390 x 272. Lithograph by W.R. Dickenson, 1835.

201. LLANGOLLEN, Birch Woods near. 341 x 276. Etching by J.G. Strutt, *c.* 1830.

202. LLANGOLLEN, in the Collection of Messrs. Agnew and Zanetti. 187 x 256. Lithograph by W.P. Sherlock after R. Wilson, RA. Published by W. Day, February 1828. Also in R. Wilson, *Six Lithographic Drawings*, 1828.

203. LLANGOLLIN in the County of Denbigh, From the Turnpike Road above the River Dee. 201 x 292. Aquatint by Paul Sandby. Published by P. Sandby, St. George's Row, 1 September 1776. Also in P. Sandby, *Twelve Views in North Wales*, 1776.

204. LLANGOLLEN from Craig y Gath, The Village of. 228 x 305. Aquatint by M.C. Prestel after J.G. Wood. Published by J.G. Wood, 39 New Bond Street, October 1793. Also in J.G. Wood, *Six Views in the Neighbourhood of Llangollen and Bala*, 1793.
CRO

205. LLANGOLLEN, Denbighshire. 102 x 151. Line engraving by J. Greig after Pearson. Published by Vernor, Hood & Sharpe, Poultry, 1 July 1810. Also in J. Evans, *The Beauties of England and Wales*, 1812.
CRO*

206. LLANGOLLEN, Denbighshire. 91 x 119. Etching.

207. LLANGOLLEN, Denbighshire. 91 x 120. Line engraving. Published by T.Tunbridge, Market St., Manchester. Also in W. Cathrall, *History of North Wales,* 1828.
CL

208. LLANGOLLEN, Denbighshire. 89 x 147. Line engraving by J.C. Varrall after H. Gastineau. Published by Jones & Co., Temple of the Muses, Finsbury Square, London, 1831. Also in *Wales Illustrated,* 1830.
CRO

209. LLANGOLLEN, Denbighshire. Mill House. 92 x 62. Line engraving.

210. LLANGOLLEN, Denbighshire, View in the Vale of. 89 x 147. Line engraving by T. Barber after H. Gastineau. Published by Jones & Co., Temple of the Muses, Finsbury Square, London. Also in *Wales Illustrated,* 1830.
CRO

211. LLANGOLLEN, A Fall on the Dee near. 226 x 303. Aquatint by M.C. Prestel after J.G. Wood. Published by J.G. Wood, 39 New Bond St., October 1793. Also in J.G. Wood, *Six Views in the Neighbourhood of Llangollen and Bala,* 1793.

212. LLANGOLLEN from the Garden of the Inn. 121 x 173. Lithograph by Thomas and Edward Gilks after D.H. McKewan. Published in L.S. Costello, *The Falls, Lakes, and Mountains of North Wales,* 1845.
CRO*

213. LLANGOLLEN, North Wales. 164 x 254. Line engraving by J.T. Willmore after J.M.W. Turner, RA. Published by Longman & Co., Paternoster Row, 1837. Also in J.M.W. Turner, *Picturesque Views in England and Wales,* 1832-8.
CRO

214. LLANGOLLEN, North Wales. 62 x 98. Line engraving by S. Lacey.

215. LLANGOLLEN, North Wales, Entrance to the Vale of. 387 x 463. Aquatint by F.J. Sarjent. Published by J.Deeley, 95 Berwick St., Soho Square, 11 May 1811.

216. LLANGOLLEN, North Wales, A Mill at. 281 x 395. Aquatint. Drawn and engraved by Day. Published by John Murphy, 19 Howland Street, Fitzroy Square, 16 August 1810.

217. LLANGOLLEN, North Wales, The Vale of. 61 x 96. Line engraving by J.Pye after G. Cuitt.

218. LLANGOLLEN, North Wales, View near. 97 x 142. Line engraving by F.R. Hay after J.P. Neale. Published by J. Harris, St. Paul's Churchyard, 1 August 1812. Also in J. Evans, *The Beauties of England and Wales,* 1812.
CRO*

219. LLANGOLLEN, Old Mill near. 257 x 182. Lithograph by Randall Druce. Printed by C. Moody, 257 High Holborn. Published in R. Druce, *Picturesque Sketches in North Wales.*

220. LLANGOLLEN, On the Streamlet crossing. 145 x 198. Aquatint by Thomas Cartwright. Published by E. Williams, Strand, 15 April 1813. Also in E. Pugh, *Cambria Depicta,* 1816.
CRO

221. LLANGOLLEN, The Town and Vale of. 185 x 275. Lithograph by G. Hawkins after G. Pickering. Printed by Day & Son. Published by T. Catherall, Eastgate Row, Chester & Bangor, 16 August 1850.
CRO

222. [LLANGOLLEN, The Vale of]. 155 x 241. Aquatint by D. Havell after T. Compton. Published by T. Compton, RMA Woolwich, 31 December 1816. Also in T. Compton, *The Northern Cambrian Mountains*, 1817.

223. LLANGOLLEN, The Vale of. 141 x 194. Line engraving by T.A. Prior after W. Harvey from a sketch by J. Thorne, *c.* 1849.
CRO

224. LLANGOLLEN, Vale of. 66 x 114. Line engraving by W. Banks & Son, Edinburgh. Published by T. Catherall, Chester and Bangor. Also in T. Catherall, *Views in North Wales, c.* 1860.

225. LLANGOLLEN, Vale of, from Barbers Hill. 199 x 285. Lithograph by Newman & Co. after H. Smyth.

226. LLANGOLLEN, Vale of, Dee Viaduct. 78 x 132. Line engraving. Published by T. Catherall, Chester. Also in E. Parry, *The Cambrian Mirror*, 1850.
CRO*

227. LLANGOLLEN, Vale of. Dee Viaduct. 209 x 404. Line engraving by H. Adlard after P. Philips. Published in *The Stationer's Almanack*, 1861.

228. LLANGOLLEN, Vale of. Dee Viaduct. Length 1508 Ft. Height 147 Ft. Number of Arches 19, Span of Arches 60 Ft. 105 x 156. Line engraving. Published by T. Catherall, Chester. Also in T. Catherall, *Views in North Wales, c.* 1860.

229. LLANGOLLEN, Vale of - Dee Viaduct. Length 1508 feet — Height 147 feet — Number of Arches 19 — Span of Arches 60 feet. 188 x 276. Lithograph by G. Hawkins after G. Pickering. Printed by Day & Son. Published by T. Catherall, Eastgate Row, Chester.

230. LLANGOLLEN, Vale of. From the Tower, Wynnstay Park. 94 x 152. Line engraving by W. Radclyffe after David Cox. Published in T. Roscoe, *Wanderings and Excursions in North Wales*, 1836.
CRO*

231. LLANGOLLEN, Vale of. From the Tower, Wynnstay Park. 104 x 141. Line engraving by S. Lacey. Published by J. Mason, 14 City Road & 66 Paternoster Row, London.

232. LLANGOLLEN, Viaduct over the Dee near. Height 148 feet: Length 1532 feet. 110 x 150. Line engraving by J. Newman, 48 Watling St. Published by Hugh Jones, Llangollen.

233. LLANGOLLEN, Viaduct over the Dee near, on the Chester & Shrewsbury Railway. 101 x 146. Line engraving.

234. LLANGOLLEN, View in the Vale of. Crow Castle in the distance. 110 x 153. Line engraving by B. Sands after C. Marshall. Published in *The Gallery of Modern British Artists*, 1834.

235. LLANGOLLEN, Weeping Birch in the Vale. 303 x 391. Lithograph and soft ground etching by J. Laporte. Published by Hassell & Co., 11 Clements Inn, London, 1 December 1812.

236. LLANGOLLEN, Bridge at. 127 x 203. Soft ground etching by G. Cumberland. Published in *A Poem on the Landscape of Great Britain*, 1793.

237. LLANGOLLENE. The Bridge and Kings Head Hotel. 117 x 174. Lithograph by W. Crane.
CRO

238. LLANGOLLEN BRIDGE. 300 x 419. Aquatint by F. Jukes after T. Walmsley. Dedicated to His Royal Highness The Prince of Wales. Published by F. Jukes, 10 Howland St., 30 January 1794. Also in T. Walmsley & F. Jukes, *Views in North Wales*, 1792-4.

239. LLANGOLLEN BRIDGE. 227 x 309. Aquatint by M.C. Prestel after J.G. Wood. Published by J.G. Wood, 39 New Bond Street, October 1793. Also in J.G. Wood, *Six Views in the Neighbourhood of Llangollen and Bala*, 1793.
CRO

240. LLANGOLLEN BRIDGE. 234 x 306. Aquatint by M.C. Prestel after J.G. Wood. Published by J.G. Wood, No. 39 New Bond Street, October 1793.
CRO

241. LLANGOLLEN BRIDGE. 52 x 82. Etching [by John Musgrove, 1810].

242. LLANGOLLEN BRIDGE. 153 x 242. Lithograph by Day & Haghe. Published by Seacome & Prichard, Chester. Also in *Recollections of a Tour through North Wales*, 1839.

243. LLANGOLLEN BRIDGE. 64 x 115. Line engraving by Rogers. Published in J. Hemingway, *Panorama of North Wales*, 1839.
CRO*

244. LLANGOLLEN BRIDGE. 171 x 242. Lithograph by W. Crane, Chester.

245. LLANGOLLEN BRIDGE. 156 x 244. Lithograph by Day & Haghe. Published by J. Seacome, Chester.

246. LLANGOLLEN BRIDGE, Denbighshire. 100 x 156. Line engraving by J. Harwood. Published by J. Harwood, 26 Fenchurch Street, 4 July 1846.

247. LLANGOLLEN & BRIDGE, Denbighshire. 75 x 90. Line engraving by Newman & Co., Watling St., London. Published in Newman & Co., *Six Views in North Wales*.

248. LLANGOLLEN BRIDGE, View from. 85 x 90. Line engraving by Newman & Co., 48 Watling Street. Published by David Roberts, Llangollen.

249. LLANGOLLEN BRIDGE, View on the River Dee from. 63 x 93. Line engraving by Edward Finden after Capt. R[obert] Batty. Published by John Murray, London, 1 August 1823. Also in R. Batty, *Welsh Scenery*, 1823.

250. LLANGOLLEN BRIDGE, West View of. 99 x 174. Photo-lithograph. Drawn and printed in the London Drawing Office, 1884.

251. LLANGOLLEN BRIDGE AND CASTELL DINAS BRAN. 121 x 198. Etching by W. Batenham.
CRO

252. LLANGOLLEN BRIDGE, CASTLE DINAS BRAN, On the River Dee, North Wales. 60 x 96. Line engraving.

253. LLANGOLLEN CHURCH. 77 x 100 diam. Aquatint.

254. LLANGOLLEN CHURCH, Denbighshire. 90 x 146. Line engraving by C. Mottram after H. Gastineau. Published by Jones & Co., Temple of the Muses, Finsbury Square, London. Also in *Wales Illustrated*, 1830.
CRO

255. LLANGOLLEN CHURCH, Denbighshire. 60 x 88. Line engraving by Rock & Co. Published 15 February 1869.

256. LLANGOLLEN, THE PARSONAGE. 101 x 160. Lithograph by W. Crane, Chester, *c.* 1840.

257. LLANGOLLEN VALE (Pl. 1). 109 x 163. Aquatint [by J. Bluck] after J.C. Ibbetson, *c.* 1795.

258. LLANGOLLEN VALE (Pl. 2). 114 x 162. Aquatint by [J.] Bluck after [J.C.] Ibbetson, *c.* 1795.

259. LLANGOLLEN VALE (Pl. 3). 109 x 158. Aquatint by [J.] Bluck after [J.C.] Ibbetson, *c.* 1795.

260. LLANGOLLEN VALE. 165 x 215. Line engraving by R. Scott after D. Thomson. Published by G. Thomson, Edinburgh, May 1809.

261. LLANGOLLEN VALE. 157 x 243. Aquatint by T. Fielding after G.F. Robson. Published by T. Clay, Ludgate Hill, London, 1 March 1820. Also in T. Compton, *The Northern Cambrian Mountains*, 1820.
CRO

262. LLANGOLLEN VALE. 82 x 113. Line engraving by W. Banks, 1850.

263. LLANGOLLEN VALE. 82 x 120. Etching by G[eorge] Cuitt. Published in G. Cuitt, *Etchings of Ancient Buildings*, 1816, and *Wanderings and Pencillings*, 1855.
CRO*

264. LLANGOLLEN VALE from Nant y Bellan, View of. 228 x 303. Aquatint by M.C. Prestel after J.G. Wood. Published by J.G. Wood, 39 New Bond St., October 1793. Also in J.G. Wood, *Six Views in the Neighbourhood of Llangollen and Bala*, 1793.
CRO

265. LLANGOLLEN VALE, View of. 128 x 181. Line engraving by S. Middiman after J. Barrett, etched by T. Tagg. Published by S. Middiman, London, 25 January 1787. Also in S. Middiman, *Select Views in Great Britain*, 1787.
CRO

266. LLANGOLLEN VALE & AQUEDUCT. 41 x 67. Line engraving. Published by T.T. & J. Tegg, Cheapside, 1 October 1832. Also in G.N. Wright, *Scenes in North Wales*, 1833.
CRO*

267. LLANGOTHLIN. 168 x 231. Aquatint by [T.] Sutherland. Published by R. Ackermann, 101 Strand, London, in *Ackermann's New Drawing Book*, 1809.

268. LLANRHAIADR HALL, East View of. 100 x 174. Photo-lithograph. Drawn and printed at the London Drawing Office, 1885.

269. LLANRHAIADR HALL, South View of. 111 x 171. Photo-lithograph. Drawn and printed at the London Drawing Office, 1885.

270. LLANROOST, Bridge at. 158 x 225. Etching by I.B.

271. LLANROOST BRIDGE, Merionethshire [*sic*]. 390 x 565. Aquatint by B. Comte after [J.] Laporte.

272. LLANROOST BRIDGE over the River Conway in North Wales. 109 x 188. Line engraving. Inigo Jones Architect. Published in *The Gentleman's Magazine*, 1753.

273. LLANRUST BRIDGE, North Wales. 103 x 151. Line engraving by [W.] Woolnoth after J.P. Neale. Published by John Harris, St. Paul's Church Yard, 1 August 1814. Also in J. Evans, *The Beauties of England and Wales*, 1812.
CRO*

274. LLANRWST. 156 x 231. Soft ground etching by J.G. Wood. Published in J.G. Wood, *The Principal Rivers of Wales*, 1813.

275. LLANRWST, Denbighshire, The Bridge at. 206 x 293. Aquatint by Paul Sandby after L. Nixon. Published by P. Sandby, St. Georges Row, Oxford Turnpike, London, 1786.

276. LLANRWST in Denbighshire, The Bridge of. 152 x 207. Line engraving by S. Sparrow after S.H. Grimm. Published by Edward Easton, 1 January 1780. Also in H.P. Wyndham, *A Tour through Monmouthshire and Wales*, 1781.
CRO*

277. LLANRWST, North Wales. 100 x 140. Line engraving by Newman & Co. Published by John Jones, Druggist, Llanrwst.

278. LLANRWST, North Wales. 226 x 317. Lithograph by Newman & Co., 48 Watling Street. Published by John Jones, Druggist, Llanrwst.

279. LLANRWST, Vale of. 52 x 76. Line engraving. Published by [H.] Humphreys, Carnarvon.

280. LLANRWST, Vale of. 70 x 100. Line engraving by Newman & Co. Published in *Seventy-two Views of North Wales*.

281. LLANRWST. Victoria Hotel. 80 x 110. Line engraving by Newman & Co. Published in *Seventy-two Views of North Wales*.

282. LLANRWST, Bridge at. 57 x 90. Line engraving by James Craig after L.F. [?Francia], *c.* 1810.

283. LLANRWST BRIDGE in 1781. 123 x 179. Lithograph by Miss W. Wynne Minshall. Printed by Woodall & Venables, Oswestry. Published in Sir J. Wynne, *History of the Gwydir Family* (1878 edition).

284. LLANRWST BRIDGE. 124 x 180. Line engraving by J. Fittler after M. Griffith. Published in T. Pennant, *A Tour in Wales*, 1784.
CRO*

285. LLANRWST BRIDGE. 74 x 124. Aquatint by Underwood after [?George] Samuel. Published by G. Sael, 192 Strand, 21 April 1797. Also in *A Collection of Welsh Tours*, 1797.
CL

286. LLANRWST BRIDGE. 109 x 167. Line engraving by J. Walker after E. Dayes. Published by J. Walker, 16 Rosomans St., 1 August 1799.
CRO

287. LLANRWST BRIDGE. 108 x 177. Line engraving by [S.] Sparrow after J. Nixon. Published by J. Sewell, Cornhill, 1 September 1790. Also with change in publisher's imprint, in C. Hulbert, *The Parlour Book of British Scenery*, 1832.

288. LLANRWST BRIDGE. 42 x 67. Line engraving by T. Gilks.

289. LLANRWST BRIDGE. 65 x 115. Line engraving by Newman & Co. Published by J. Jones, Llanrwst. Also in *Seventy-two Views of North Wales*.

290. LLANRWST BRIDGE. 123 x 178. Line engraving by Page.

291. LLANRWST BRIDGE built by Inigo Jones. 93 x 147. Line engraving by I. Thomas after H. Gastineau. Published in *Wales Illustrated*, 1830.
CRO

292. LLANRWST BRIDGE, North Wales. 90 x 125. Line engraving by W. Birch after P. Reinagle. Published by W. Birch, Hampstead Heath, 1 May 1789.
CRO

293. LLANRWST BRIDGE, North Wales. 90 x 150. Line engraving. Published by J. & F. Harwood, 26 Fenchurch Street, 24 January 1842. Also in J. & F. Harwood, *A Volume of Views of North Wales, c.* 1846.

294. LLANRWST CHURCH. 115 x 171. Lithograph by George Cuitt, 1815.

295. LLANRWST CHURCH. 41 x 67. Line engraving. Published by T.T. & J. Tegg, Cheapside, 1 October 1832. Also in G.N. Wright, *Scenes in North Wales,* 1833.
CRO*

296. LLANRWST CHURCH, Denbighshire. 92 x 148. Line engraving by I. Thomas after H. Gastineau. Published in *Wales Illustrated*, 1830.
CRO

297. LLANSILIN CHURCH. 159 x 210. Lithograph by J. Evans after T. Bailey.

298. LLANSILLIO in Denbighshire, the Seat of Thomas Jones, Esq. 96 x 163. Line engraving by J. Walker after W. Evans. Published by H.D. Symonds, No. 20, Allen & West, No. 15 Paternoster Row, & T. Conder, No. 30 Bucklersbury, London, 23 April 1796.
CRO

299. LLANSILLIO in Denbighshire, the Seat of Thomas Jones, Esq. 106 x 165. Line engraving by [J.] Walker after [W.] Evans. Published by Harrison & Co., 18 Paternoster Row, London, 1 February 1788. Also in *Picturesque Views of the Principal Seats of the Nobility and Gentry,* 1787-8.

300. LLANTISILIO, near Llangollen. Old Farm House at. 258 x 182. Lithograph by Randall Druce. Printed by C. Moody, 257 High Holborn. Published in R. Druce, *Picturesque Sketches in North Wales.*

301. LLANTISILIO CHURCH, Vale of Llangollen, Denbighshire. 94 x 151. Line engraving by H. Adlard after H. Gastineau. Published in *Wales Illustrated,* 1830.
CRO

302. LLEWENEY, Bleach Works belonging to the late Honbl. Thomas Fitzmaurice. 409 x 584. Aquatint by T. Malton after T. Walmsley and T. Sandby, RA. Dedicated to the Corporation of Liverpool by T. Walmsley.

303. LLEWENNI, Denbighshire, Bleach Works at, as at first intended to be built, For the Honble Thomas Fitzmaurice. Line engraving by W.Watts after T.Sandby. 123 x 180. Published by J. & J. Boydell, Cheapside & at the Shakspeare Gallery, Pall Mall, 25 June 1792. Also in R.C. Hoare, *Forty-Eight Views of Noblemen's and Gentlemen's Seats,* 1795. CRO

304. LLEWENY in Denbighshire, View of the Bleach Works at. 98 x 170. Line engraving by W. Bromley after John Bird. Published by J. Sewell, Cornhill, 1 March 1789.

305 LLEWENY HALL in Denbighshire. The Seat of the Honble. Thomas Fitzmaurice. 130 x 186. Line engraving by W. Angus after J. Bird. Published by W. Angus, 4 Gwynne's Buildings, Islington, 1 January 1789. CRO

306. LLEWENNI HALL, Denbighshire. The Seat of the Honble. Thomas Fitzmaurice. 126 x 182. Line engraving by W. Watts after M. Griffith. Published by J. & J. Boydell, Cheapside, & at the Shakspeare Gallery, Pall Mall, 25 June 1792. Also in R.C. Hoare, *Forty-Eight Views of Noblemen's and Gentlemen's Seats,* 1795. CRO

307. LLEWENNI HALL, Denbighshire. The Seat of the Honble. Thomas Fitzmaurice. 122 x 179. Line engraving by W. Watts after M. Griffith. Published by J. & J. Boydell, Cheapside, & at the Shakspeare Gallery, Pall Mall, 25 June 1792. Also in R.C. Hoare, *Forty-Eight Views of Noblemen's and Gentlemen's Seats,* 1795. CRO

308. NANT Y BELA. 143 x 195. Aquatint by T. Cartwright after E[dward] Pugh. Published by E. Williams, Strand, 15 May 1813. Also in E. Pugh, *Cambria Depicta,* 1816. CRO*

309. NANT Y BELAN, 305 x 430. Aquatint by F. Jukes after T. Walmsley. Dedicated to John Strange, Esqr. Published by F. Jukes, 10 Howland St., 31 May 1794. Also in T. Walmsley & F. Jukes, *Views in North Wales,* 1792-4.

310. NANT Y BELLAN. 156 x 231. Soft ground etching by J.G. Wood. Published in J.G. Wood, *The Principal Rivers of Wales,* 1813.

311. NANT Y BELLON, Wynstay, Denbighshire, A Scene near. 299 x 224. Lithograph [by C. Marsh] after T[homas] B[arker]. Published in T. Barker, *Thirty-two Lithographic Impressions of Landscape Scenery,* 1814.

312. NANT-Y-BELAN AND VALE OF LLANGOLLEN. 79 x 111. Wood engraving. Reproduced from J.S. Howson, *The River Dee,* 1875, and published in A. Roberts, *Wynnstay and the Wynns,* 1876. CL

313. NEW BRIDGE, The, on the River Dee near Chirk Castle. 130 x 181. Line engraving by Peter Mazell after Paul Sandby. Published by G. Kearsly, Fleet Street, London, 1 February 1779. Also in P. Sandby, *The Virtuosi's Museum,* 1778. CRO

314. PENSARN, Abergele. 72 x 95. Line engraving by Newman & Co. Published by R. Jones, Abergele.

315. PENTRE FELIN, near Llangollen. 301 x 424. Aquatint by F. Jukes after T. Walmsley. Published by F. Jukes, Howland Street, 20 January 1794. Dedicated to Rt. Hon. Lady Eleanor Butler and Miss Ponsonby. Also in T. Walmsley & F. Jukes, *Views in North Wales*, 1792-4.

316. PENTRE MAWR, Denbighshire, The seat of John Jones Bateman, Esq. 160 x 252. Lithograph by J. Shaw after C.J. Greenwood.

317. PEN-Y-LAN. 232 x 359. Lithograph by Maclure, Macdonald & Macgregor, London. CRO

318. PEN-Y-LAN across the Dee, View of. 222 x 302. Aquatint by W. Ellis after E. Pugh. Dedicated to Rt. Hon. Lord Kenyon. Published by E. Pugh, Great Queen Street, Lincoln's Inn Fields, 24 November 1794.

319. PICKHILL HALL. 290 x 410. Lithograph by Waterlow & Sons, London, 13 July 1872.

320. PICKHILL HALL [Lodge]. 161 x 231. Lithograph by Waterlow & Sons, London, 1872.

321. PILLAR OF ELISEG. 103 x 100. Line engraving by P. Mazell after M. Griffith. Published in T. Pennant, *A Tour in Wales*, 1778. CRO*

322. PILLAR OF ELISEG, Valle Crucis. 152 x 98. Line engraving by F. Cary after D. Parkes, 25 June 1808. Published in *The Gentleman's Magazine*, 1809.

323. PILLAR OF ELISEG. 108 x 74. Etching. Drawn and etched by A. Clint. Published by H. Colburn, 13 Gt. Marlborough Street. Published in G.J. Bennett, *A Pedestrian Tour Through North Wales*, 1838. CRO*

324. PILLAR OF ELISEG. 96 x 50. Line engraving. Published in J. Parry, *A Trip to North Wales made in 1839* (1840). CRO*

325. PILLAR OF ELISEG. 120 x 93. Photo-lithograph [after E.H. Lloyd], 1881.

326. PILLAR OF ELISEG near Valle Crucis Abbey. 205 x 155. Lithograph.

327. PISTYLL RAYDR. A fall of 240 Feet. 215 x 301. Aquatint. Published by Laurie & Whittle, 53 Fleet Street, London, 12 September 1799.

328. PISTILL RHAIADR. 795 x 370. Line engraving by J. Lewis.

329. PISTILL RHAIADR. 278 x 192. Line engraving.

330. PISTILL RHAIADR, North Wales. 245 x 184. Lithograph.

331. PISTILL RHAIADR, A Great Cataract in North Wales. 195 x 109. Line engraving. Published in *The Gentleman's Magazine*, 1750.

332. PISTYLL RHAIADR. 492 x 345. Line engraving by J. Green after J. Evans. Dedicated to the Rt. Hon. Henry Arthur Herbert, Earl of Powis. Published 27 April 1794.

333. PISTYLL RHAIADR. 151 x 100. Line engraving by [J.] Storer after [E.] Dayes. Published for Longman & Rees, 14 May 1804. Also in W. Bingley, *North Wales*, 1804.
CL

334. [PISTYLL RHAIADR]. 156 x 228. Aquatint by T. Baily after T. Compton. Published by T. Compton, RMA Woolwich, 15 September 1815. Also in T. Compton, *The Northern Cambrian Mountains*, 1820.

335. PISTYLL RHAIADR. 82 x 69. Line engraving by Newman & Co., *c.* 1860.

336. PISTYLL RHAIADR. Depth of the Fall 240 Feet. 139 x 97. Line engraving by Perkins & Bacon. Published by J. Rodwell, New Bond Street, June 1832.

337. PISTYLL RHAIADYR. 160 x 218. Aquatint by I. Baily, drawn by T. Compton. Published by T. Clay, 18 Ludgate Hill, London, 2 March 1818. Also in T. Compton, *The Northern Cambrian Mountains*, 1820.

338. PLAS NEWYDD. 106 x 135. Line engraving by S. & G. Nicholson, Liverpool. Published in S. & G. Nicholson, *Plas Newydd and Vale Crucis Abbey*, 1824.
CRO*

339. PLAS NEWYDD. 42 x 67. Line engraving. Published by T.T. & J. Tegg, Cheapside, 1 October 1832. Also in G.N. Wright, *Scenes in North Wales*, 1833.
CRO*

340. PLAS NEWYDD. 74 x 100 diam. Line engraving by Newman & Co., 69 Southwark Bridge Rd., 28 March 1880.

341. PLAS NEWYDD, A cottage near Llangollen, Denbighshire. 74 x 97 diam. Line engraving by W. Thomas. Published in *The European Magazine*, 1794.

342. PLAS NEWYDD, Denbighshire. 111 x 160. Line engraving by J. Newman, 48 Watling St. Published by R. Hughes & Son, Wrexham.
CRO

343. PLAS NEWYDD, Denbighshire. 60 x 90. Line engraving by Newman & Co. Published and sold by David Roberts, Llangollen.

344. PLAS NEWYDD, The Elegant Retirement of Lady Eleanor Butler and Miss Ponsonby. 75 x 100 diam. Line engraving by J. L. after J.G. Wood. Published in J.G. Wood, *Six Views in the Neighbourhood of Llangollen and Bala*, 1793.

345. PLAS NEWYDD, Entrance to. The Residence of the Right Honble Lady Eleanor Butler and Miss Ponsonby. 135 x 106. Line engraving by S. & G. Nicholson, Liverpool. Published by R. Ackermann, 101 Strand. Published in S. & G. Nicholson, *Plas Newydd and Vale Crucis Abbey*, 1824.
CRO*

346. PLAS NEWYDD. Entrance to. The Residence of The Right Honble. Lady Eleanor Butler and Miss Ponsonby. 236 x 175. Lithograph by John McGahey, Bank Buildings, Castle St., Liverpool. Published by T. Catherall, Eastgate Row, Chester, London: Ackermann & Co., Strand; Dublin: T. Cranfield, Westmorland Street. Also in J. Hicklin, *The Ladies of Llangollen*, 1847.

347. PLAS NEWYDD, Font in the Grounds of. 115 x 85. Etching. Drawn and etched by A. Clint. Published by H. Colburn, 13 Gt. Marlborough Street. Also in G.J. Bennett, *A Pedestrian Tour Through North Wales*, 1838.
CRO*

348. PLAS NEWYDD, Llangollen. 135 x 235. Lithograph. Drawn and printed by W. Crane, Chester.

349. PLAS NEWYDD, Llangollen. Dedicated by permission to the Right Hon. Lady Eleanor Butler & Miss Ponsonby by . . . H. Billinge. 125 x 222. Lithograph by J.W. Guy after H. Billinge. Printed by Geo. Smith, Liverpool.

350. PLAS NEWYDD, near Llangollen, Denbighshire. The Seat of Lady Eleanor Butler and Miss Ponsonby. 100 x 149. Line engraving by [W.] Woolnoth after J.P. Neale. Published by John Harris, St. Paul's Churchyard, 1 May 1813. Also in J. Evans, *The Beauties of England and Wales*, 1812.
CRO*

351. PLAS NEWYDD, near Llangollen, Denbighshire. 91 x 151. Line engraving by H. Jorden after H. Gastineau. Published in *Wales Illustrated*, 1830.
CRO

352. PLAS NEWYDD, near Llangollen. The Seat of the late Lady Eleanor Butler and Miss Ponsonby. 199 x 270. Lithograph by W.L. Walton after E.W. Jacques. Hullmandel & Walton, lithographers. Published by T. Catherall, Bookseller, Chester. Also in J. Hicklin, *The Ladies of Llangollen*, 1847.

353. PLAS NEWYDD, near Llangollen. The residence of the late Lady Eleanor Butler & Miss Ponsonby. 45 x 65. Line engraving by T. Gilks.

354. PLAS NEWYDD, near Llangollen. The Seat of the late Lady Eleanor Butler and Miss Ponsonby. 201 x 277. Lithograph by W. [L.] Walton after Edwin W. Jacques, respectfully inscribed by permission to the Present Ladies. Printed by C. Hullmandel.
CL

355. PLAS YN GREEN, Denbighshire. Seat of George Naylor, Esq. 160 x 248. Lithograph by J. Shaw after C.J. Greenwood.

356. PONT CYSSYLLTAU AQUEDUCT, Denbighshire. 104 x 153. Wood engraving by J. & H.S. Storer after H. Hughes. Published by T. Catherall, Chester. Also in W. Cathrall, *History of North Wales*, 1828.
CL

357. [PONTCYSYLLTE AQUEDUCT]. Part of the Aqueduct that crosses Llangothlin Vale. 108 x 152 diam. Aquatint by J. Bluck after J. Baker. Published in J. Baker, *A Picturesque Guide Through Wales and the Marches*, 1795.

358. PONT CYSYLLTE AQUEDUCT, North Wales. 419 x 586. Aquatint by F. Jukes after J. Parry. Published by J. Parry, Bryn y Fynnon, Wrexham, 1 March 1806. Sold by Messrs. Clay & Scriven, Ludgate Hill, & Messrs. Colnaghi & Co., print merchants, Cockspur Street, London.

359. PONTCYSYLLTE AQUEDUCT, Denbighshire. 152 x 225. Lithograph by C. Hullmandel after H. Walter. Published by T. Clay, Ludgate Hill, London, 1 February 1821. Also in T. Compton, *The Northern Cambrian Mountains*, 1820.

360. PONTCYSYLLTY, AQUEDUCT AT. 147 x 292. Soft ground etching by J.G. Wood. Pubished in J.G. Wood, *The Principal Rivers of Wales*, 1813.

361. PONT CYSYLLTY AQUEDUCT. 104 x 133. Aquatint by J. Havell after E. Pugh. Published by E. Williams, Strand, 15 November 1814. Also in E. Pugh, *Cambria Depicta*, 1816.
CRO*

362. PONT Y CASULLTE AQUEDUCT in the Vale of Llangollen, Denbighshire. This Aqueduct 1007 feet in length carries the waters of the Ellesmere Canal over the River Dee. 67 x 102. Line engraving after T.H. Shepherd. Published in T. Dugdale, *England and Wales Delineated*, 1854-60.
CRO

363. PONT Y CASULLTE AQUEDUCT in the Vale of Llangollen. 61 x 98. Line engraving by John Pye after W. Havell.

364. PONT Y CYSLTE AQUEDUCT, North Wales. 125 x 198. Lithograph after G. Pickering. Published by J. Seacome, Bookseller, Chester. Printed by Engelmann & Co. Also in G. Pickering, *Four Picturesque Views in North Wales.*
CRO

365. PONT Y CYSSYLTAU, Aqueduct over the Dee called. 59 x 89. Line engraving by Edward Finden after Capt. R[obert] Batty. Published by John Murray, London, 1 January 1823. Also in R. Batty, *Welsh Scenery*, 1823.
CL

366. PONT Y CYSSYLLTE in the Vale of Llangollen, Denbighshire. 90 x 151. Line engraving by J.C. Varrall after H. Gastineau. Published in *Wales Illustrated*, 1830.
CRO

367. PONT Y CYSYLLTE in the Vale of Llangollen, Denbighshire. 105 x 165. Line engraving by J. Newman, 48 Watling St. Published by Hugh Jones, Llangollen.
CRO

368. PONT Y CYSYLTE, L'aqueduc de, dans le Pays de Galles. 222 x 328. Line engraving by Adam.

369. PONT YCHEL, Ruthin. 129 x 177. Line engraving by William Poole after Edward Pugh. Published by E. Pugh & W. Poole, 1 September 1795.
CRO

370. PONT DWFFYS. 175 x 124. Etching.

371. PONT GLYN DYFFWS between Corwen and Cyrniogen Mawr. 300 x 222. Lithograph [by C. Marsh] after T[homas] B[arker]. Published in T. Barker, *Thirty-Two Lithographic Impressions of Landscape Scenery*, 1814.

372. PONT Y GLYN near Cerig y Druidian, Denbighshire. 142 x 84. Line engraving by J.B. Allen after H. Gastineau. Published in *Wales Illustrated*, 1830.
CRO

373. PONT Y GLYN near Corwen, Merionethshire. 200 x 112. Etching by J.B. Knight, 1816. Published in *The Gentleman's Magazine*, 1816.

374. PONT Y GLYN, 6 miles from Corwen, N. Wales. 277 x 200. Lithograph after E.W. Jacques.

375. [PONT Y GLYN-DIFFWYS]. Waterfall near Corwen. Glyn Dipwys. 93 x 77. Line engraving by Newman & Co. Published by E. Edwards, Corwen.

376. PONT Y GLYN DYFFID, Corwen, Merionethshire. 304 x 419. Aquatint by S. Alken after [Rev.] B. Broughton. Published by F. Jukes, London, 1 July 1800.

377. PONT Y GLYN DYFFIS, near Corwen. 158 x 226. Aquatint by S. Alken after Rev. B. Broughton. Published by J. Mawman, Poultry, 13 April 1801. Also in Rev. B. Broughton, *Six Picturesque Views in North Wales*, 1801.

378. GLYN near Corwen. 153 x 117 diam. Aquatint after J. Baker. Published in J. Baker, *A Picturesque Guide through Wales and the Marches*, 1795.

379. GLYN DYFFWYS near Corwen, Part of. 301 x 225 diam. Aquatint by M.C. Prestel after J.G. Wood. Published by J.G. Wood, 39 New Bond Street, October 1793. Also in J.G. Wood, *Six Views in the Neighbourhood of Llangollen and Bala*, 1795.

380. POOL PARK, near Ruthin, The Seat of Lord Bagot. 66 x 98. Line engraving by Newman & Co. Published by J. Clarke, Ruthin. Also in W. Davis, *Hand-Book for the Vale of Clwyd*, 1856.
CRO*

381. ROSSET MILL, The, Trevallyn, [Lower Marford Mill]. 210 x 310. Etching by Sidney Massie, 1821.

382. RHUABON, Denbighshire. 93 x 150. Line engraving by H. Adlard after H. Gastineau. Published in *Wales Illustrated*, 1830.
CRO

383. ROABBON, near Wrexham, View at. 284 x 413. Aquatint by [T.] Cartwright after [T.] Walmesley. Published by James Daniell, 480 Strand, 29 May 1810.

384. RUTHIN. 156 x 230. Soft ground etching by J.G. Wood. Published in J.G. Wood, *The Principal Rivers of Wales*, 1813.

385. RUTHIN. 41 x 67. Line engraving. Published in G.N. Wright, *Scenes in North Wales*, 1833.
CRO*

386. RUTHIN. 348 x 794. Line engraving by I. Lewis.

387. RUTHIN, Denbighshire. 127 x 182. Line engraving by W. Poole after E. Pugh, 1 September 1795.
CRO

388. RUTHIN, Denbighshire. Town Hall. 91 x 149. Line engraving by W. Wallis after H. Gastineau. Published in *Wales Illustrated*, 1830.
CRO

389. RUTHIN. The Market Place. 45 x 85. Line engraving. Published by I. Clarke, Ruthin. Entered at Stationers' Hall. Also in W. Davis, *Hand-Book for the Vale of Clwyd*, 1856.
CRO*

390. RUTHIN. St. Peter's Church. 53 x 91. Line engraving. Published in W. Davis, *Hand-Book for the Vale of Clwyd*, 1856.
CRO*

391. RUTHIN CASTLE. 41 x 68. Line engraving. Published by T.T. & J. Tegg, Cheapside, 1 October 1832. Also in G.N. Wright, *Scenes in North Wales*, 1833.
CRO*

392. RUTHIN CASTLE. 75 x 108. Line engraving by W. Banks, 1855.

393. RUTHIN CASTLE. 105 x 155. Line engraving by Newman & Co. Published by T. Catherall, Chester.

394. RUTHIN CASTLE. 112 x 160. Aquatint after J. Baker.

395. RHUTHIN CASTLE in the County of Denbigh, The South West View of. 148 x 352.
Line engraving by S. and N. Buck, 9 April 1742. Published in S. and N. Buck, *Views
of all the Castles*, 1742.
CRO

396. RUTHIN CASTLE in the County of Denbigh, The South West View of. 73 x 139.
Line engraving. Published in *A Description of England and Wales*, 1769.
CRO

397. RUTHIN CASTLE, Denbighshire. 96 x 152. Line engraving by W. Radclyffe after H.
Gastineau. Published in *Wales Illustrated*, 1830.
CRO

398. RUTHIN CASTLE, Denbighshire. 76 x 110. Line engraving by W. Banks, Edinburgh.
Sold by James Jones, Ruthin. Published by T. Catherall, Chester and Bangor. Also in
T. Catherall, *Views in North Wales, c.* 1860.

399. RUTHIN CASTLE, Denbighshire, North West View of Buildings Recently Erected.
201 x 302. Lithograph by Day & Son. Henry Clutton, Architect, May 1852.
CRO

400. RUTHIN CASTLE, Denbighshire. South-West View of Buildings Recently Erected.
204 x 303. Lithograph by Day & Son. Henry Clutton, Architect, May 1852.
CRO

401. RUTHIN CASTLE, Denbighshire, South-West View of Buildings Recently Erected.
202 x 303. Lithograph by F. Bedford. Printed by Day & Son. Published by T.
Catherall, Chester and Bangor, 1 March 1853.

402. RUTHIN CASTLE, Denbighshire. South West View of Buildings Recently Erected.
72 x 98. Line engraving by Newman & Co. Published by J. Clarke, Ruthin. Also in
W. Davis, *Hand-Book for the Vale of Clwyd*, 1856.
CRO*

403. RUTHIN CASTLE, Denbighshire. South West View of Buildings Recently Erected.
75 x 102. Line engraving by Newman & Co. Published in *Seventy-two Views of
North Wales*.

404. RUTHIN CASTLE. Mr. John Clutton, Architect. 162 x 268. Line engraving.
Published in *The Builder* (Vol. XI), 1865.
CRO

405. RUTHIN CASTLE, N.W. View of. 68 x 93. Line engraving by Newman & Co.
Published by J. Clarke, Ruthin. Also in W. Davis, *Hand-Book for the Vale of Clwyd*,
1856.
CRO*

406. RUTHIN MILL, Denbighshire. 104 x 163. Line engraving by H. Longueville Jones
after J.H. Le Keux, 1856. Published in *Archaeologia Cambrensis*, 1856.
CRO*

407. RUTHIN SCHOOL (North Wales). 60 x 89. Line engraving by [J.] Storer after John
Hughes. Published in T. Evans, *Walks Through Wales*, 1819.
CL

408. STANSTY HALL, Denbighshire, The Seat of Richard Thompson, Esqr. 158 x 252.
Lithograph by J. Shaw. Published by C.J. Greenwood.
CRO

409. TANYROGO. 63 x 90. Line engraving by Rock & Co., London.

410. TANYROGO, Denbighshire, View from the Cave. 60 x 70. Line engraving by Rock & Co., London, 14 September 1857.

411. TANYROGO, near Abergele, Denbighshire, The Cave at. 70 x 83. Line engraving by Rock & Co., London, 18 September 1857.

412. TANYROGO, Gates at. 60 x 88. Line engraving by Rock & Co., London.

413. TREFALYN HALL, Denbighshire, The Seat of Thomas Griffith, Esqre. 163 x 248. Lithograph by J. Shaw. Published by C.J. Greenwood.
CRO

414. TREVALLYN HALL. 148 x 224. Lithograph by Henry Grueber. Printed by Engelmann, Graf, Coindet & Co. Published in H. Grueber, *Six Lithographic Views of Seats in the Neighbourhood of Wrexham, North Wales.*

415. TREVALYN HALL, Denbighshire. 83 x 125. Line engraving by C. Pye after J.P. Neale. Published by W.H. Reid, London, April 1818. Also in J.P. Neale, *Views of the Seats of Noblemen*, 1818-23.
CRO

416. TREFNANT. Holy Trinity Church, Interior of. 114 x 150. Photo-lithograph by A. Macgregor (late Maclure & Co.), Liverpool, 1874. Published in D.R. Thomas, *History of the Diocese of St.Asaph*, 1874.
CRO*

417. TREVOR HALL, Denbighshire. 104 x 161. Line engraving by [J.] Walker after [W.] Evans. Published by J. Walker, 16 Rosaman's Street, London, 1 April 1795.
CRO

418. TYN-Y-PISTYLL, near Llangollen. The Britannia Inn. 259 x 183. Lithograph by Randall Druce. Printed by C. Moody, 257 High Holborn. Published in R. Druce, *Picturesque Sketches in North Wales.*

419. VALE OF CRUCIS, View of a Fall on the Dee near. 227 x 304. Aquatint by W. Ellis after E. Pugh. Dedicated to Sir Watkin Williams Wynn, Bart., M.P. Published by E. Pugh, now of Great Queen Street, Lincoln's Inn Fields, 24 November 1794.
CRO

420. VAL CRUCIS ABBEY, Denbighshire. 130 x 234. Lithograph by W.A. Frank.

421. VAL CRUCIS ABBEY. 125 x 95. Line engraving by T. Gilks. Published in L.S. Costello, *The Falls, Lakes and Mountains of North Wales.*
CRO*

422. VALE CRUCIS ABBEY. The Domestic Buildings. 188 x 260. Lithograph by Randall Druce. Printed by C. Moody, 257 High Holborn. Published in R. Druce, *Picturesque Sketches in North Wales.*

423. VALE CRUCIS ABBEY, East End of, From the Interior. 122 x 94. Line engraving by S. & G. Nicholson. Printed by R. Ackermann, 101 Strand, London. Published in S. & G. Nicholson, *Plas Newydd and Vale Crucis Abbey*, 1824.
CRO*

424. VALE CRUCIS ABBEY, East View of. 135 x 105. Line engraving by S. & G. Nicholson. Published by R. Ackerman, 101 Strand. Also in S. & G. Nicholson, *Plas Newydd and Vale Crucis Abbey*, 1824.
CRO*

425. VALE CRUCIS [ABBEY], East Window. 137 x 224. Lithograph. Printed and published by W. Potter & Co., Carnarvon. Also in W. Crane, *Picturesque Scenery in North Wales*, 1842.

426. VALE CRUCIS ABBEY, Exterior, East End. 185 x 248. Lithograph by Randall Druce. Printed by C. Moody, 257 High Holborn. Published in R. Druce, *Picturesque Sketches in North Wales*.

427. VALE CRUCIS ABBEY, Interior, Looking East. 185 x 255. Lithograph by Randall Druce. Printed by C. Moody, 257 High Holborn. Published in R.Druce, *Picturesque Sketches in North Wales*.

428. VALE CRUCIS ABBEY, Interior, Looking West. 259 x 185. Lithograph by Randall Druce. Printed by C. Moody, 257 High Holborn. Published in R. Druce, *Picturesque Sketches in North Wales*.

429. VALE CRUCIS ABBEY near Llangollen. 160 x 241. Lithograph by L. Haghe. Printed by Day & Haghe. Published by J. Seacome, Chester.
CRO

430. VALE CRUCIS ABBEY, N. Wales. [Doorway]. 185 x 137. Etching by J.S. Cotman, 8 September 1810.

431. VALE CRUCIS ABBEY, On the Road to. 257 x 182. Lithograph by Randall Druce. Printed by C. Moody, 257 High Holborn. Published in R. Druce, *Picturesque Sketches in North Wales*.

432. VALE CRUCIS ABBEY, Remains of the Chapel. 135 x 105. Line engraving by S. & G. Nicholson. Published by R. Ackerman, 101 Strand. Also in S. & G. Nicholson, *Plas Newydd and Vale Crucis Abbey*, 1824.
CRO*

433. VALE CRUCIS ABBEY, Vale of Llangollen. 61 x 96. Line engraving.

434. VALE CRUCIS ABBEY, West View of. 135 x 105. Line engraving by S. & G. Nicholson. Published in S. & G. Nicholson, *Plas Newydd and Vale Crucis Abbey*, 1824.
CRO*

435. VALE CRUCIS ABBEY, West Window. 167 x 225. Lithograph by D. George. Published by W. Potter & Co., Carnarvon. Also in W. Crane, *Picturesque Scenery in North Wales*, 1842.

436. VALE CRUSIS ABBEY. 226 x 557. Line engraving by Robert Baugh [part of John Evans, *Map of the Six Counties of North Wales*, 1795].
CRO*

437. VALLA CRUSSES, near Llangollin, belonging to Sir Watkin Williams Wynn, Bart. 214 x 290. Aquatint. Published by J. Boydell, Cheapside, London, September 1779.

438. VALLE CRUCIS. 147 x 224. Lithograph.

439. VALLE CRUCIS, North Wales. 280 x 383. Lithograph by W.R. D[ickenson]. Published by J. Dickenson.

440. VALLE CRUCIS ABBEY. 103 diam. Line engraving by J. Ryland [after B. Ralph]. Published in *England Illustrated*, 1764.

441. VALLE CRUCIS ABBEY. 75 x 102. Aquatint by G.J. Parkyns. Published by G.J. Parkyns, 1 November 1791. Also in J. Moore & G.J. Parkyns, *Monastic Remains and Ancient Castles*, 1792.

442. VALLE CRUCIS ABBEY. 102 x 166. Aquatint by S. Alken after Rev. W. Bingley. Published in W. Bingley, *A Tour Round North Wales*, 1800.
CL

443. [VALLE CRUCIS ABBEY]. 96 x 143. Aquatint by J. Bluck. Published by John P. Thompson, Gt. Newport St.,12 March 1808.

444. VALLE CRUCIS ABBEY. 83 x 128. Wood engraving by H. Hughes. Printed by J. Johnson, Apollo Press, Brook St., Holborn. Published in H. Hughes, *The Beauties of Cambria*, 1823.
CRO*

445. VALLE CRUCIS ABBEY. 94 x 64. Line engraving by Edward Finden after Capt. Robert Batty. Published by John Murray, London, 1 May 1823. Also in R. Batty, *Welsh Scenery*, 1823.

446. VALLE CRUCIS ABBEY. 95 x 94. Line engraving by J. Godfrey after J.E. Gregan, *c.* 1830. Published in *Archaeologia Cambrensis*, 1846.
CRO

447. VALLE CRUCIS ABBEY. 41 x 67. Line engraving. Published by T.T. & J. Tegg, Cheapside, 1 October 1832. Also in G.N. Wright, *Scenes in North Wales*, 1833.
CRO

448. VALLE CRUCIS ABBEY. 99 x 144. Line engraving by A. Willmore after W.H. Bartlett. Published in G. Virtue, *A Tourist in Wales*, 1835.
CRO*

449. VALLE CRUCIS ABBEY, near Llangollen. 95 x 151. Line engraving by W. Radclyffe after D. Cox. Published in T. Roscoe, *Wanderings and Excursions in North Wales*, 1836.
CRO

450. [VALLE CRUCIS ABBEY]. 131 x 182. Line engraving by J. Morris after Paul Sandby. Published by C. Hulbert, Shrewsbury. Also in C. Hulbert, *The History and Description of the County of Salop*, 1837.

451. VALLE CRUCIS ABBEY. 85 x 126. Etching. Drawn and etched by A. Clint. Published by H. Colburn, 13 Gt. Marlborough Street. Also in G.J. Bennett, *A Pedestrian Tour Through North Wales*, 1838.
CRO*

452. VALLE CRUCIS ABBEY. 204 x 264. Line engraving by J. Newman. Published by R. Hughes & Son, Wrexham, *c.* 1860.

453. VALLE CRUCIS ABBEY, East View. 83 x 174. Photo-lithograph after E.H. Lloyd, 1881.

454. VALLE CRUCIS ABBEY. 115 x 160. Line engraving by J. Newman, 48 Watling Street. Published by R. Hughes & Son, Wrexham.
CRO

455. VALLE CRUCIS ABBEY. 76 x 110. Aquatint by G. Cuit, junr.

456. VALLE CRUCIS ABBEY. 77 x 102. Aquatint.

457. VALLE CRUCIS ABBEY. 153 x 109 diam. Aquatint.

458. VALLE CRUCIS ABBEY. 88 x 104. Line engraving.

459 VALLE CRUCIS ABBEY, Denbighshire. 100 x 152. Line engraving by Daniel Lerpinière, 15 April 1776. [Later state of No. 476]. Published in F. Grose, *The Antiquities of England and Wales*, 1786.

460. VALLE CRUCIS ABBEY, Denbighshire. 111 x 164. Line engraving by James Storer after J. Varley. Published by J. Walker, 16 Rosomans Street, London, 1 October 1800.
CRO

461. VALLE CRUCIS ABBEY, Denbighshire. 171 x 246. Aquatint by J. Harriden after Miss Smirke. Published by R. Bowyer, 87 Pall Mall, 1820. Also in Miss Smirke, *Six Welsh Views, c.* 1808.

462. VALLE CRUCIS ABBEY, Denbighshire. 59 x 90. Line engraving by W. Backshell after C. Marshall, 1812.

463. VALLE CRUCIS ABBEY, Denbighshire. 100 x 152. Line engraving by J. Greig after [J.S.] Storer. Published by J. Harris, St. Paul's Churchyard, 1 July 1812. Also in J. Evans, *The Beauties of England and Wales*, 1812.
CRO

464. VALLE CRUCIS ABBEY, Denbighshire. 65 x 100. Line engraving by J. & H.S. Storer after J. Roe. Published by Sherwood & Co., 1 October 1823.

465. VALLE-CRUCIS ABBEY, Denbighshire. 91 x 147. Line engraving by W. Radclyffe after H. Gastineau. Published in *Wales Illustrated*, 1830.
CRO

466. VALLE CRUCIS ABBEY, Denbighshire. 159 x 236. Line engraving by J.C. Varrall after J.M.W. Turner, RA. Published by Robert Jennings, Poultry, 1 March 1828. Also in J.M.W. Turner, *Picturesque Views in England and Wales*, 1832-8.
CRO

467. VALLE CRUCIS ABBEY in Denbighshire. 132 x 181. Line engraving by Thornton. Published by Alexander Hogg, 16 Paternoster Row, *c.* 1790.
CRO

468. VALLE CRUCIS ABBEY, Denbighshire, Near. 179 x 244. Etching by F. Stevens after J. Cristall. Published at R. Ackermann's, 101 Strand, 1 May 1815.

469. VALLE CRUCIS ABBEY, Denbighshire. 60 x 89. Line engraving by F.W. Topham after W. Havell.

470. VALLE CRUCIS ABBEY, Denbighshire, The River Dee near. 62 x 99. Line engraving by John Pye after W. Havell.

471. VALLE CRUCIS ABBEY, East End of. 155 x 217. Soft ground etching by J.G. Wood. Published in J.G. Wood, *The Principal Rivers of Wales,* 1813.

472. VALLE CRUCIS ABBEY, East End of. Interior. 173 x 99. Photo-lithograph. Drawn and printed at the London Drawing Office, 1884.

473. VALLE CRUCIS ABBEY, East View of. 101 x 176. Photo-lithograph. Drawn and printed at the London Drawing Office, 1885.

474. VALLE CRUCIS ABBEY in 1835, Sketch of. 188 x 289. Lithograph by D. George.

475. VALLE CRUCIS ABBEY looking East. 111 x 175. Photo-lithograph. Drawn and printed at the London Drawing Office, 1885.

476. VALLE CRUCIS ABBEY, Llan Egwiste or Llanegwast, The Abbey of, Denbeighshire. 99 x 151. Line engraving by D[aniel] L[erpinière] after S. Hooper, 15 April 1776. Published in F. Grose, *The Antiquities of England and Wales,* 1776.
CRO

477. [VALLE CRUCIS ABBEY]. The Abbey of Llan Egwerst or Vale Crucis and Castle Dinas Bran. 203 x 287. Aquatint by Paul Sandby. Published by P. Sandby, St. Georges Row, 1 September 1776. Also in P. Sandby, *Twelve Views in North Wales,* 1776.

478. [VALLE CRUCIS ABBEY]. Abbey of Llan Egwerst. 130 x 183. Line engraving by J. Morris after P. Sandby. Published by G. Kearsly, Fleet Street, 1 August 1779. Also in P. Sandby, *The Virtuosi's Museum,* 1778.
CRO

479. VALLE CRUCIS ABBEY or Llanegwast, West Side. 57 x 87. Line engraving by Edward Finden after Capt. R[obert] Batty. Published by John Murray, London, 1 May 1823. Also in R. Batty, *Welsh Scenery,* 1823.
CL

480. VALLE CRUCIS ABBEY, Llangollen. 77 x 52. Line engraving. Published by Humphreys, Caernarvon.

481. VALLE CRUCIS ABBEY, Llangollen, Denbighshire. 65 x 95. Line engraving by Rock & Co., 15 February 1869. Published in Rock & Co., *Picturesque Views in North Wales,* 1871.

482. VALLE CRUCIS ABBEY, near Llangollen. 82 x 129. Line engraving. Published by G. Prichard, Chester. Also in J. Hicklin, *Illustrated Handbook of North Wales,* 1853.
CRO*

483. VALLE CRUCIS ABBEY, near Llangollen. 175 x 245. Lithograph.

484. VALLE CRUCIS ABBEY, near Llangollen. 201 x 278. Lithograph by W. Walton after E.W. Jacques. Printed by C. Hullmandel.

485. VALLE CRUCIS ABBEY, near Llangollen, Denbighshire. 139 x 192. Lithograph. Drawn and printed by W. Crane, Chester.

486. VALLE CRUCIS ABBEY, near Llangollen, North Wales. 61 x 95. Line engraving by J. Pye after G. Cuitt.

487. VALLE CRUCIS ABBEY, North Wales. 110 x 185. Etching by H.W.

488. VALLE CRUCIS ABBEY in Wales. 100 x 164. Line engraving. Published by Bowles and Carver, 69 St. Paul's Church Yard, London.

489. VALLE CRUCIS ABBEY, West End of. [Interior]. 173 x 99. Photo-lithograph. Drawn and printed at the London Drawing Office, 1884.

490. VALLE CRUCIS ABBEY, West Front. 340 x 253. Photo-lithograph after Lloyd-Williams and Underwood. Published in Lloyd-Williams & Underwood, *Village Churches of Denbighshire*, 1872.
CRO*

491. VALLE CRUCIS ABBEY, West View. 93 x 175. Photo-lithograph [after E.H. Lloyd], 1881.

492. VALLE CRUCIS ABBEY, West View of. 173 x 100. Photo-lithograph. Drawn and printed at the London Drawing Office, 1884.

493. VALLE CRUCIS ABBY. 139 x 207. Line engraving. Published in T. Pennant, *A Tour in Wales*, 1778.
CRO*

494. VALLE CRUCIS ABBY. 135 x 203. Line engraving by P. Mazell after M. Griffith. Published in T. Pennant, *A Tour in Wales*, 1778.
CRO*

495. VALLE CRUCIS ABBY in the County of Denbigh, The East View. 148 x 360. Line engraving by S. & N. Buck, 9 April 1742. Published in S. and N. Buck, *Views of all the Castles*, 1742.
CRO

496. VALLE CRUCIS ABBY in the County of Denbigh, The West View. 148 x 360. Line engraving by S. & N. Buck, 9 April 1742. Published in S. & N. Buck, *Views of all the Castles*, 1742.
CRO

497. VALLE-CRUCIS ABBEY. 76 x 102. Aquatint. Drawn and engraved by J. Hassell. Published by J. Hassell, 1 July 1807.
CRO

498. VALLE CRUSIS ABBEY. 96 x 159. Lithograph by J. Baynes. Printed by C. Hullmandel. Published by Radwell & Martin, New Bond Street, London, 18 February 1823.

499. VALLE CRUSIS ABBEY, Denbighshire. 96 x 149. Line engraving by J. Storer after E. Pratt, 1810. Published in J. Evans, *The Beauties of England and Wales*, 1812.
CRO

500. VALLEY CRUCIS ABBEY. 175 x 254. Lithograph by G. Hawkins after G. Pickering. Published by T. Catherall, East Gate Row, Chester. Lithograph by Day & Son, Chester, 1850. Also in J. Hicklin, *Ladies of Llangollen*, 1847.

501. VALLEY CRUCIS ABTEI. 142 x 97. Line engraving. Published by E. Kollmann, Leipzig, 1873.

502. VALLI CRUCIS ABBEY. 60 x 92. Line engraving.

503. VALLIS CRUCIS in Denbighshire, A Landscape of the Country which surrounds the Abbey of. 150 x 211. Line engraving by W. Walker and W. Angus after S.H. Grimm. Published by Edward Easton, 1 March 1781. Also in H.P. Wyndham, *A Tour Through Monmouthshire and Wales*, 1781.
CRO*

504. ABBEY CRUSIS near Llangollen, View of. 299 x 415. Aquatint by F. Jukes after T. Walmsley. Dedicated to Rt. Hon. Countess of Orkney. Published by F. Jukes, 10 Howland St., London, 30 January 1794. Also in T. Walmsley & F. Jukes, *Views in North Wales*, 1792-4.

505. ABBEY CRUSIS, North Wales. 502 x 619. Aquatint by F. Jukes after T. Walmsley. Published by F. Jukes, 10 Howland St., 1 June 1800.

506. ASH, VALE CRUSIS ABBEY, North Wales. 340 x 300. Lithograph by George Barnard.

507. CRUCIS ABBEY, near Llangollen. 92 x 125. Lithograph. Drawn and printed by W. Crane, Chester.

508. VOELAS, The Seat of the Honble. Mrs. Charles Finch. 100 x 154. Aquatint by J. Baker.

509. [WIGFAIR]. East End of Capel Vair, Wygfair, near St. Asaph. 91 x 141. Lithograph. Published in M.L. Louis, *Gleanings in North Wales*, 1854.
CRO*

510. WREXHAM. 148 x 251. Lithograph by Henry Burn. Printed by McLean & Co., 70 St. Martins Lane, London. Published by Thomas Painter, Wrexham, October 1847.

511. WREXHAM. 74 x 100. Wood engraving.

512. WREXHAM in the County of Denbigh, The South View of. 245 x 781. Line engraving by S. and N. Buck, Garden Court, 1 Middle Temple, 8 September 1748. Published in S. & N. Buck, *Buck's Antiquities: or Venerable Remains*, 1774.

513. WREXHAM, Denbighshire. [Pentre'r Felin]. 59 x 79. Line engraving by J. Greig after Arthur Harrison. Published by W. Clarke, New Bond St., 1 August 1817. Also in *Antiquarian Itinerary*, Vol. VI., 1817.
CRO

514. WREXHAM, Denbighshire. 94 x 149. Line engraving by W. Wallis after H. Gastineau. Published in *Wales Illustrated*, 1830.
CRO

515. WREXHAM, Denbighshire. 40 x 58 diam. Line engraving by Newman & Co. Published by E. Hughes & Son, Wrexham.

516. WREXHAM, Denbighshire. 106 x 140. Line engraving by J. Newman. Published by R. Hughes, Wrexham.

517. [WREXHAM. Grove Park School]. 95 x 152. Line engraving [by Newman & Co. Published by R. Hughes & Son, Wrexham].
CRO

518. WREXHAM. [Mount Street]. 90 x 61. Line engraving by Edward Finden after R[obert] Batty. Published in R. Batty, *Welsh Scenery*, 1823.
CL

519. WREXHAM. [Mount Street]. 101 x 72. Line engraving. Published in G.A. Cooke, *A Topographical and Statistical Description of North Wales, c. 1830.*
CL

520. WREXHAM. A Prospect of the North-side of the Church and Steeple of Wrexham in Denbigh-shire North Wales. Dymma llûn tûr Gogleddeglwys a Chlochty Gwrexham yn Shir Ddinbech. 418 x 475. Line engraving by Thos. Bradshaw Jnr. Dedicated to the Honble. William Robinson Esqr. Member of Parliament for Denbigh in the county of Denbigh, *c.* 1707.

521. WREXHAM CHURCH. 112 x 160. Aquatint by J. Ross after J. Baker. Published in J. Baker, *A Picturesque Guide through Wales and the Marches, 1795.*

522. WREXHAM CHURCH. 83 x 127. Wood engraving by Hugh Hughes. Published in H. Hughes, *The Beauties of Cambria, 1823.*
CRO*

523. WREXHAM CHURCH. 62 x 87. Line engraving. Published in *Wrexham Registrar,* 1850.

524. WREXHAM CHURCH, Denbighshire, North Wales. 199 x 270. Lithograph. Drawn and printed by W. Crane, Chester. Published by R. Hughes, Bookseller, Church St., Wrexham.

525. WREXHAM CHURCH. 389 x 308. Lithograph by P. Gauci from a painting by E. Jones, Architect.

526. WREXHAM CHURCH. 197 x 142. Line engraving. Published in *Our Own Country,* Vol. 1.

527. WREXHAM CHURCH. 122 x 170. Lithograph.

528. WREXHAM CHURCH in the County of Denbigh, The North-East View of. 391 x 522. Line engraving by J. Boydell. Dedicated to the Hon. Sir Watkin Williams Wynn, Bart. Published & sold by J. Boydell at the Globe near Durham Yard in the Strand & by Tho. Payne, Bookseller at Wrexham, 1748.

529. WREXHAM CHURCH, Denbighshire. 123 x 180. Line engraving by W. Watts after M. Griffith. Published by J. & J. Boydell, Cheapside & at the Shakspeare Gallery, Pall Mall, 25 June 1792. Also in R.C. Hoare, *Forty-Eight Views of Noblemen's and Gentlemen's Seats, 1795.*
CRO

530. WREXHAM CHURCH, Denbighshire, Tower of. 151 x 94. Line engraving by W. Wallis after H. Gastineau. Published in *Wales Illustrated,* 1830.
CRO

531. WREXHAM CHURCH in Denbighre, N. Wales, A North View of. 117 x 155. Line engraving by J. Fernal, Watchmaker, Wrexham, *c.* 1780.

532. WREXHAM CHURCH, Eastern View of [from Mount Street]. 305 x 221. Lithograph by J.W. Walton after Frederick Peake. Printed by Day & Haghe. Published by Thomas Painter, Wrexham, 1843.

533. WREXHAM CHURCH [Interior]. 132 x 108. Photo-lithograph after A. Baker. Architect for the Restoration (1867) B. Ferrey. Published in D.R. Thomas, *History of the Diocese of St. Asaph,* 1874.
CRO

534. WREXHAM CHURCH, Interior View of. 154 x 116. Lithograph. Drawn and printed by W. Crane, Chester. Published in W. Cathrall, *History of North Wales*, 1828.
CL

535. WREXHAM CHURCH, North View of. 163 x 199. Line engraving by J. Barlow. Published by Richard Taylor, Church Street, Liverpool.
CRO

536. WREXHAM CHURCH, North Wales. 320 x 419. Aquatint by T. Cartwright after Joseph Allen. Dedicated to Sir Foster Cunliffe, Bart., *c.* 1830.

537. WREXHAM CHURCH TOWER. 178 x 105. Lithograph, 1885.

538. WREXHAM DISPENSARY, North East View of. 103 x 187. Edward Welsh, architect. Lithograph by James Bell, Lord Street, Liverpool, *c.* 1838.
CRO

539. WREXHAM, SAINT GILE'S, DENBIGHSHIRE. 436 x 282. Lithograph by A. Newman after Charles Wickes. Plate No. 7. Printed by Day & Son.
CRO

540. WYNNESTAY. 130 x 177. Wood engraving by W.H.J. Boot. Published in J.S. Howson, *The River Dee*, 1875.
CRO*

541. WYNNESTAY. 148 x 225. Lithograph by Henry Grueber. Printed by Engelmann, Graf, Coindet & Co. Published in H. Grueber, *Six Lithographic Views of Seats near Wrexham, North Wales*.

542. WYNNSTAY. 41 x 67. Line engraving. Published by T.T. & J. Tegg, Cheapside, 1 October 1832. Also in G.N. Wright, *Scenes in North Wales*, 1833.
CRO

543. WYNNSTAY. 130 x 177. Wood engraving by W.H.J. Boot. Published in A. Roberts, *Wynnstay and the Wynns*, 1876.

544. WYNNSTAY. 130 x 184. Chromo-lithograph [by Frank Lydon]. Published in F.O. Morris, *Picturesque Views of Seats of the Noblemen*, *c.* 1880.
CRO

545. WYNN STAY. 55 x 95. Line engraving by Neele & Son. Published by S. Leigh, Strand.

546. WYNNSTAY, Denbighshire. 107 x 166. Line engraving by Birrell after Evans. Published by J. Walker, 16 Rosomans Street, London, 1 March 1792.
CRO

547. WYNNSTAY, Denbighshire. 103 x 160. Line engraving by Birrell after Evans. Published by Harrison & Co., 18 Paternoster Row, 1 March 1792.
CRO

548. WYNN STAY, Denbighshire. The Seat of Sir Watkin Williams Wynne. 167 x 229. Lithograph by F. Calvert. Printed by C. Hullmandel. Published by T. Hughes, 35 Ludgate St., June 1821.

549. WYNNSTAY, Denbighshire. 86 x 128. Line engraving by T. Barber after J.P. Neale. Published by J.P. Neale, 16 Bennet Street, Blackfriars' Road, 1 January 1829. Also in J.P. Neale, *Views of the Seats of Noblemen*, 1824-9.

550. WYNNSTAY, Denbigh Shire. 99 x 152. Line engraving.
CRO

551. WYNNSTAY, Denbighshire. 103 x 155. Line engraving by J. Newman, 48 Watling St. Published by R. Hughes & Son, Wrexham.
CRO

552. WYNNSTAY, Denbighshire. Sir W.W. Wynn, Bt. 40 x 62. Line engraving.

553. WYNN STAY in Denbighshire. The Seat of Sir Watkin Williams Wynn, Bart. 131 x 184. Line engraving by M.A. Rooker after Paul Sandby. Published by G. Kearsly in Fleet Street, 1 January 1775. Also in P. Sandby, *A Collection of One Hundred and Fifty Select Views*, 1781.
CRO

554. WYNNSTAY in Denbighshire. The Seat of Sir Watkin Williams Wynn, Bart. 104 x 161. Line engraving by Birrell after Evans. Published by Harrison & Co., 18 Paternoster Row, 1 September 1788. Also in *Picturesque Views of the Principal Seats of the Nobility*, 1787-8.

555. WYN-STAY in Denbighshire. The Seat of Sir Watkin Williams Wynne, Bart. 90 x 161. [Line engraving by M.A. Rooker after Paul Sandby]. Published in *The Lady's Magazine*, 1770-1832.

556. WYNSTAY on the River Dee, At. 171 x 240. Etching. Drawn and engraved by F.C. Lewis, 1845.

557. WYNNSTAY, Seat of Sir Watkin Williams Wynn, Bart., From a Cottage above the New Bridge over the River Dee, Denbigh Shire. 205 x 295. Aquatint by Paul Sandby. Published by P. Sandby, St. Georges Row, 1 September 1776. Also in P. Sandby, *Twelve Views in North Wales*, 1776.

558. WYNNSTAY, The Seat of Sir W.W. Wynne, Bart., Denbighshire. 95 x 150. Line engraving by S. Lacey after H. Gastineau. Published in *Wales Illustrated*, 1830.
CRO

559. WYNNESTAY PARK, View in. 106 x 152 diam. Aquatint.

560. WYNNSTAY PARK, Avenue in. 84 x 54. Wood engraving. Reproduced from J.S. Howson, *The River Dee*, 1875. Published in A. Roberts, *Wynnstay and the Wynns*, 1876.
CRO*

ADDENDA

561. VALLE CRUCES ABBEY. 75 x 92. Line engraving by Newman & Co. Published in Newman & Co., *Six Views in North Wales*.

562. DENBIGH. GOBLIN TOWER. 106 x 159. Line engraving. Published in J. Williams, *Ancient and Modern Denbigh*, 1856.
CRO*

563. DENBIGH. Royal Bowling Green. 113 x 175. Line engraving. Published in J. Williams, *Ancient and Modern Denbigh*, 1856.
CRO*

564. DENBIGH. Ruin of Old St. David's. 102 x 181. Line engraving. Published in J. Williams, *Ancient and Modern Denbigh*, 1856.
CRO*

565. DENBIGH CASTLE. 111 x 163. Line engraving by G.H. Published in J. Williams, *Ancient and Modern Denbigh*, 1856.
CRO*

566. LLANRWST CHURCH, New, Denbighshire. 390 x 330. Lithograph by J.R. Jobbins after Henry Kennedy. Dedicated to the Revd. Thomas Griffith Roberts, Chairman of the Committee for erecting the Church, by Henry Kennedy, Architect.
CRO

601. BACHEGRAIG, near Denbigh: a residence of Sir Richard Clough. 88 x 147. Etching after Rev. A.B. Clough, *c.* 1860.

602. BACHEGRIG HOUSE, Flintshire. 101 x 151. Line engraving by [R.] Godfrey after Samuel Hooper, 25 February 1776. Published in F. Grose, *The Antiquities of England and Wales*, 1786.
CRO

603. BACHEGRIG HOUSE in the County of Flint [with account]. 101 x 150. Line engraving by [R.] Godfrey after Samuel Hooper, 25 February 1776. Published in F. Grose, *The Antiquities of England and Wales*, 1776.
CRO

604. BAGILLT HALL. 102 x 182. Line engraving by J. Barlow after J. Ingleby. Published by B. & J. White, 1 January 1796. Published in T. Pennant, *History of Whiteford and Holywell*, 1796.
CRO

605. BANGOR CHURCH & BRIDGE. 104 x 150. Line engraving by [S.] Sparrow after S. Hooper, 29 September 1786. Published in F. Grose, *The Antiquities of England and Wales*, 1786.
CRO

606. BANGOR ISCOED, Flintshire. 91 x 145. Line engraving by T. Barber after H. Gastineau. Published in *Wales Illustrated*, 1830.
CRO

607. BANGOR UPON DEE. 156 x 231. Soft ground etching by J.G. Wood. Published in J.G. Wood, *The Principal Rivers of Wales*, 1813.
CRO

608. BASINGWERK ABBEY. 194 x 240. Line engraving by P.C. Canot after M. Griffith. Published in T. Pennant, *A Tour in Wales*, 1778.
CRO*

609. BASINGWERK ABBEY. 142 x 238. Line engraving by J. Caldwall after M. Griffith. Published in T. Pennant, *A Tour in Wales*, 1778.
CRO*

610. BASINGWERK ABBEY. 76 x 107. Aquatint by G.J. Parkyns. Published by G.J. Parkyns, 1 December 1791. Also in J. Moore & G.J. Parkyns, *Monastic Remains and Ancient Castles*, 1792.
CRO

611. BASINGWERK ABBEY. 106 x 152. Aquatint by I. Wright. Published in J. Baker, *A Picturesque Guide through Wales and the Marches*, 1795.

612. BASINGWERK ABBEY. 76 x 108. Aquatint. Engraved and published by J. Hassell, 1 August 1807.

613. BASINGWERK ABBEY. 158 x 228. Soft ground etching by J.G. Wood. Published in J.G. Wood, *The Principal Rivers of Wales*, 1813.

614. BASINGWERK ABBEY. 84 x 128. Wood engraving by Hugh Hughes. Published in H. Hughes, *The Beauties of Cambria*, 1823.
CRO*

615. BASINGWERK ABBEY. 56 x 93. Line engraving by W. Batenham, Chester. Published in A. Batenham, *The Travellers' Companion ... from Chester through North Wales,* 1825.
CRO*

616. BASINGWERK ABBEY. 120 x 200. Line engraving. Published by T. Catherall, Chester.
CRO

617. BASINGWERK ABBEY, Flintshire. 60 x 86. Line engraving by J. Greig after Edward Dayes, 1 April 1808. Published by W. Clarke, New Bond St., and J. Carpenter, Old Bond Street. Also in *Antiquarian and Topographical Cabinet,* 1807-11.
CRO

618. BASINGWERK ABBEY, Flintshire. 90 x 150. Line engraving by H. Jorden after H. Gastineau. Published in *Wales Illustrated,* 1830.
CRO

619. BASINGWERK ABBEY, Flintshire. 165 x 246. Line engraving [? by Rev. J. Brooke] , 1868.
CRO

620. BASINGWERK ABBEY, Flintshire. 73 x 121. Line engraving by S. Lacey. Published by J. Mason, 14 City Road & 66 Paternoster Row.
CRO

621. BASINGWERK ABBEY (S.W. View). 100 x 178. Lithograph by J.H.L. [? John Henry Le Keux] , 1846. Published in *Archaeologia Cambrensis,* 1846.
CRO*

622. BASINGWERK ABBY in the County of Flint, the North West View of. 143 x 347. Line engraving by S. and N. Buck, 9 April 1742. Published in S. and N. Buck, *Views of all the Castles,* 1742.
CRO

623. BASINGWERK MONASTERY, Flintshire, North-Wales [with account] . 104 x 153. Line engraving by [S.] Sparrow, 29 July 1774. Published in F. Grose, *The Antiquities of England and Wales,* 1776.

624. BASINGWERK MONASTERY, Flintshire. 105 x 153. Line engraving by [S.] Sparrow, 29 July 1774. Published in F. Grose, *The Antiquities of England and Wales,* 1786.
CRO

625. BASINGWERK MONASTERY, Flintshire. 53 x 70. Aquatint [octagonal] .

626. BASINGWERK MONASTERY in Flintshire. 78 x 100. Line engraving. [Engraved and published by Alexander Hogg, 16 Paternoster Row] .
CRO

627. BESINGWERK ABBEY. 78 x 100. Line engraving by Newman & Co., 69 Southwark Bridge Road, London, 1878.

628. [BODELWYDDAN] . 148 x 242. Lithograph by W. Stanley, *c.* 1825.

629. [BODELWYDDAN] . 180 x 267. Lithograph by W. Stanley, *c.* 1825.

630. BODELWYDDAN. 62 x 94. Line engraving by Newman & Co. Published in W. Davis, *Hand-Book for the Vale of Clwyd,* 1856.
CRO*

631. BODELWYDDAN (Near Rhyl). St. Margaret's Church. [Interior]. 293 x 225. Lithograph.

632. BODELWYDDAN (Near Rhyl). St. Margaret's Church. [N.E. View of]. 307 x 223. Lithograph.

633. BODELWYDDAN, St. Margaret's. 155 x 126. Photo-lithograph. Published in D.R. Thomas, *History of the Diocese of St. Asaph,* 1874.
CRO*

634. BODELWYDDAN CHURCH, near Abergele, The Interior. 82 x 75. Line engraving by Newman & Co. Published by Robert Jones, Visitor Office, Abergele.

635. BRONWYLFA, near St. Asaph. 73 x 82. Line engraving by J.H. Kernot after F. Hemans. Published by William Blackwood & Sons, Edinburgh & London. Also in *The Poems of Felicia Hemans,* 1859.

636. BROUGHTON HALL, Flintshire. 114 x 186. Lithograph. Printed by Standidge & Co., London.
CRO

637. BRYN ASAPH, Flintshire, S.E. View of. The residence of the Misses Luxmoore. 115 x 188. Lithograph by Paul Gauci after Thomas Jones, Architect, Chester. Printed by Graf & Soret, *c.* 1840.
CRO

638. BRYN ASAPH, Flintshire, S.W. View of. The residence of the Misses Luxmoore. 114 x 188. Lithograph by Paul Gauci after Thomas Jones, Architect, Chester. Printed by Graf & Soret, *c.* 1840.
CRO

639. BRYNBELLA, The Seat of G. Piozzi, Esqr. 110 x 162. Aquatint by J. Bluck after J. Baker. Published in J. Baker, *A Picturesque Guide through Wales and the Marches,* 1795.

640. BRYN BELLA or Mrs. Piozzi's House. 114 x 165. Aquatint by T. Cartwright after E. Pugh. Published by E. Williams, Strand, 15 June 1814. Also in E. Pugh, *Cambria Depicta,* 1816.
CRO

641. BRINAPREECE in Flintshire, The Seat of Francis Parry Price, Esq. 103 x 160. Line engraving by [W.] Thomas after [W.] Evans. Published by Harrison & Co., 18 Paternoster Row, 1 May 1788. Also in *Picturesque Views of the Principal Seats of the Nobility,* 1786-8.
CRO

642. BRYN-Y-PYS, Flintshire, The Seat of Francis Richard Price, Esqr. 162 x 244. Lithograph by C.J. Greenwood.
CRO

643. BRYN-Y-PYS, Flintshire. The Seat of Francis Richard Price, Esqr. [N.W. View]. 162 x 245. Lithograph by C.J. Greenwood.

644. BYCHTON. 70 x 105 diam. Line engraving by W. Angus after M. Griffith. Published in T. Pennant, *History of Whiteford and Holywell,* 1796.
CRO*

645. CAERGWRLE, Flintshire. 85 x 143. Line engraving by M.J. Starling after H. Gastineau. Published in *Wales Illustrated,* 1830.
CRO

646. CAERGWRLE CASTLE. 66 x 102 diam. Line engraving by P. Mazell after M. Griffith. Published in T. Pennant, *A Tour in Wales,* 1778.
CRO*

647. CAERGWRLE CASTLE. 140 x 198. Aquatint by T. Cartwright after E. Pugh. Published by E. Williams, Strand, 15 May 1814. Also in E. Pugh, *Cambria Depicta,* 1816.
CRO

648. CAERGWRLE CASTLE, N[orth] W[ales]. 263 x 353. Lithograph by W.R. D[ickenson], 1835.

649. CAERGWRLEY CASTLE in the County of Flint, the North West View of. 143 x 350. Line engraving by S. and N. Buck, 9 April 1742. Published in S. and N. Buck, *Views of all the Castles,* 1742.
CRO

650. CAERGWRLEY CASTLE in the County of Flint, The North West View of. 74 x 138. Line engraving [after Buck]. Published in *A Description of England and Wales,* 1769.

651. CAERGWRLEY CASTLE, North West View. 95 x 175. Photo-lithograph after E.H. Lloyd, 1881.

652. CLWYDDIAN HILLS, From Newmarket. 105 x 132. Aquatint by J. Havell after E. Pugh. Published by E. Williams, Strand, 15 January 1814. Also in E. Pugh, *Cambria Depicta,* 1816.
CRO*

653. CŴM, near St. Asaph. 75 x 80. Line engraving by J.H. Kernot after F. Hemans. Published in *The Poems of Felicia Hemans,* 1859.

654. CYMMAU'S, Kate of, Cottage. 103 x 135. Aquatint by T. Cartwright after E. Pugh. Published by E. Williams, Strand, 15 September 1814. Also in E. Pugh, *Cambria Depicta,* 1816.
CRO

655. DEE & MERSEY, The Estuaries of the. 146 x 200. Aquatint by T. Cartwright after E. Pugh. Published by E. Williams, Strand, 15 March 1814. Also in E. Pugh, *Cambria Depicta,* 1816.
CRO*

656. DOWNING. 82 x 135. Line engraving by [J.] Barlow. Published in T. Pennant, *History of Whiteford and Holywell,* 1796.
CRO*

657. DOWNING. 125 x 200. Line engraving by [W.] Angus after M. Griffith. Published by B. & J. White, 1 January 1796. Published in T. Pennant, *History of Whiteford and Holywell,* 1796.
CRO

658. DOWNING, Flintshire. 86 x 128. Line engraving by [H.] W. Bond after J.P. Neale. Published by J.P. Neale, 16 Bennett Street, Blackfriars Road, 1 August 1829. Also in J.P. Neale, *Views of the Seats of Noblemen,* 1818-23.
CRO

659. DOWNING, Flintshire, Mr. Pennant's Mill at. 98 x 145. Line engraving by [F.R.] Hay after F. Grose. Published by Vernor, Hood & Sharpe, Poultry, May 1811, for J. Evans, *Beauties of England and Wales*, 1812.
CRO

660. DOWNING, Grounds near. 128 x 202. Line engraving by W. Angus after M. Griffith. Published in T. Pennant, *History of Whiteford and Holywell*, 1796.
CRO*

661. DOWNING, The Seat of Thos. Pennant, Esqr., Flintshire. 118 x 180. Line engraving by W.C. Wilson after M. Griffith. Published by J. & J. Boydell, Cheapside & at the Shakspeare Gallery, Pall Mall, 25 June 1792. Also in R.C. Hoare, *Forty-Eight Views of Noblemen's and Gentlemen's Seats*, 1795.
CRO

662. DISERT is a part of Flintshire bordering on the Sea Northward... 380 x 778. Line engraving by J. Lewis. Dedicated to the Honble. Lt. Col. James Russel Stapleton.

663. DYSERTH (Flints.), N. Wales. 185 x 241. Photo-lithograph after V.H. Darwin, 1860.
CRO

664. DYSERTH, View near. 145 x 194. Aquatint by T. Cartwright after E. Pugh. Published by E. Williams, Strand, 15 July 1813. Also in E. Pugh, *Cambria Depicta*, 1816.
CRO*

665. DYSERTH CASTLE, Flintshire, Remains of. 86 x 142. Line engraving by J.C. Varrall after H. Gastineau. Published by Jones & Co., Temple of the Muses, Finsbury Square, London, 1831. Also in *Wales Illustrated*, 1830.
CRO

666. DYSERTH WATERFALL. 98 x 71. Line engraving by Newman & Co., 48 Watling St., London. Published by D. Ll. Lewis, Rhyl. Also in W. Davis, *Hand-Book for the Vale of Clwyd*, 1856.
CRO*

667. ELWY, View on the. 118 x 222. Aquatint by T. Cartwright after E. Pugh. Published by E. Williams, Strand, 15 October 1813. Also in E. Pugh, *Cambria Depicta*, 1816.
CRO*

668. EULO CASTLE. 83 x 143. Etching. Drawn and engraved by T. Bailey, 1835.
CRO

669. EULOE CASTLE, N. View. 66 x 95. Etching. Drawn and engraved by T. Bailey, *c.* 1835.

670. FLINT. 92 x 150. Line engraving by S. Lacey after H. Gastineau. Published in *Wales Illustrated*, 1830.
CRO

671. FLINT from Park Gate. 110 x 165. Line engraving by J. Walker after [J.M.] W. Turner. Published by J. Walker, 16 Rosomans Street, London, 1 August 1797.
CRO

672. FLINT, View of, in 1826 ... 94 x 75. Etching[by Sidney Massie]. Published in H. Taylor, *Historic Notices of Flint*, 1883.
CRO*

673. FLINT CASTLE. 158 x 241. Line engraving after M. Griffith. Published in T. Pennant, *A Tour in Wales*, 1778.
CRO

674. FLINT CASTLE. 81 x 113. Aquatint. Engraved and published by G. Parkyns, 1 March 1792. Published in J. Moore & G.J. Parkyns, *Monastic Remains and Ancient Castles*, 1792.
CRO

675. FLINT CASTLE [with account]. 106 x 154. Line engraving by J[ames] Newton published by S. Hooper, 27 March 1786. Also in F. Grose, *The Antiquities of England and Wales*, 1797.
CRO

676. FLINT [CASTLE]. 70 x 116. Line engraving by T. Tagg after W. Turner, *c.* 1810.
CRO

677. FLINT CASTLE. 147 x 222. Soft ground etching by J.G. Wood, 1813. Published in J.G. Wood, *The Principal Rivers of Wales*, 1813.
CRO

678. FLINT CASTLE. 153 x 241. Aquatint by T.H. Fielding after S. Prout and T. Girtin. Published by T. Clay, 18 Ludgate Hill, London, 1 July 1820. Also in T. Compton, *The Northern Cambrian Mountains,* 1820.

679. FLINT CASTLE. 140 x 192. Aquatint by T.H. Fielding. Published by T. McLean, 26 Haymarket, 1823. Also in T.H. Fielding, *British Castles*, 1825.

680. FLINT CASTLE. 127 x 191. Aquatint. Published by Thomas McLean, Haymarket, 1822. Also in T. McLean, *A Picturesque Description of North Wales*, 1823.

681. FLINT CASTLE. 76 x 114. Line engraving by G.B. [George Baxter], 1830. Published in A. Batenham, *The Traveller's Companion . . . from Chester through North Wales*, *c.* 1833.
CRO*

682. FLINT CASTLE. 90 x 145. Line engraving by S. Lacey after H. Gastineau. Published by Jones & Co., Temple of the Muses, Finsbury Square, London, 1830. Also in *Wales Illustrated*, 1830.
CRO

683. FLINT CASTLE. 42 x 72. Line engraving. Published by T.T. & J. Tegg, Cheapside, 1 October 1832. Also in G.N. Wright, *Scenery in North Wales*, 1833.
CRO*

684. FLINT CASTLE. 96 x 142. Line engraving by W. Radclyffe after J. Wrightson. Published in T. Roscoe, *Wanderings and Excursions in North Wales*, 1836.
CRO

685. FLINT [CASTLE]. 41 x 76. Octagonal line engraving.

686. FLINT CASTLE. 189 x 274. Collograph after J.M.W. Turner. Published in J. Ruskin, *Lectures on Landscape.*

687. [FLINT CASTLE]. CASTELL FFLINT. 96 x 142. Line engraving by W. Radclyffe after J. Wrightson. Published by William Mackenzie, Llundain, Llynlleifiad ac Abertawy. Also in G. ap Rhys, *Hanes y Brytaniaid a'r Cymry*, 1872-4. [cf. No.684].
CRO

688. FLINT-CASTLE, An East View of. 269 x 376. Aquatint. Published by W. Green, 3 Earl Lane, Manchester.

689. FLINT CASTLE, Flintshire. 65 x 55 diam. Line engraving.

690. FLINT CASTLE, The Keep from the South-West ... 168 x 97. Etching by L.R. [Louise Rayner]. Published in H. Taylor, *Historic Notices of Flint*, 1883.
CRO*

691. FLINT CASTLE, N.E. View of. 108 x 153. Line engraving by J. and H.S. Storer after G. Pickering. Published in W. Cathrall, *History of North Wales*, 1828.
CRO

692. FLINT CASTLE. North Wales. 102 x 150. Line engraving by [James] Roberts, 7 February 1775. Published in F. Grose, *The Antiquities of England and Wales*, 1776. [cf. No. 693].
CRO

693. FLINT CASTLE. 102 x 150. Line engraving by [James] Roberts, 7 February 1775. Published in F. Grose, *The Antiquities of England and Wales*, 1786.
CRO

694. FLINT CASTLE, North Wales. 305 x 396. Aquatint. Published by R. Reeve, 151 Grafton St. East, Fitzroy Square, London, 1 July 1812.

695. FLINT CASTLE, North Wales. 95 x 141. Line engraving by C. Pote after J.P. Neale. Published by John Harris, St. Paul's Churchyard, 1 April 1813. Also in J. Evans, *The Beauties of England and Wales*, 1812.
CRO

696. FLINT CASTLE, North Wales. 162 x 234. Line engraving by James H. Kernot after J.M.W. Turner, RA. Published by Longman & Co., Paternoster Row. Printed by McQueen, 1836. Also in J.M.W. Turner, *Picturesque Views in England and Wales*, 1832-8.
CRO

697. FLINT CASTLE. Pl.2. 106 x 154. Line engraving by J. Newton. Published by S. Hooper, 27 March 1786. Also in F. Grose, *The Antiquities of England and Wales*, 1786.
CRO

698. FLINT CASTLE, The South East View of. 145 x 348. Line engraving by S. and N. Buck, 9 April 1742. Published in S. and N. Buck, *Views of all the Castles*, 1742.
CRO

699. FLINT CASTLE, The South East View of. 110 x 220. Line engraving [after Buck]. Published in *England Display'd*, 1769.
CRO

700. FLINT CASTLE, The South East View of. 74 x 140. Line engraving [after Buck]. Published in *A Description of England and Wales*, 1769.

701. FLINT CASTLE (1840), The Remains of. 90 x 132. Line engraving by John Woods after G.F. Sargent. "Go to the rude ribs of that antient castle", *King Richard 2nd.* Act 3, Scene 3. Published by How & Parsons, 132 Fleet Street, 1 June 1841. [Plate to an edition of Shakespeare, 1841].
CRO

702. FLINT CASTLE. *Richard II*, Act III, Scene III. 98 x 159. Line engraving by [S.] Sparrow after F. Grosse [sic]. Published by E. Harding, 132 Fleet Street, 1 July 1790. Also in F. Grose, *The Antiquities of England and Wales,* 1797.
CRO

703. FLINT CASTLE, View of the Eastern Tower, from the Courtyard . . . 118 x 95. Etching by L.R. [Louise Rayner]. Published in H. Taylor, *Historic Notices of Flint,* 1883.
CRO*

704. FLINT CASTLE, View from the Eastern Tower . . . 125 x 94. Etching. Originally in *Our Own Country.* Reproduced in H. Taylor, *Historic Notices of Flint,* 1883.
CRO*

705. FLINT CASTLE, View of the Ruins of. 177 x 73. Etching by L.R. [Louise Rayner]. Published in H. Taylor, *Historic Notices of Flint,* 1883.
CRO*

706. FLINT CASTLE, West Tower viewed from East Tower. 128 x 95. Line engraving. Published in *Our Own Country.*

707. FLINT, Cornist. R. Muspratt Esqr. 189 x 289. Line engraving. Douglas & Fordham, Architects, Chester, June 1885.
CRO

708. FLINT CHURCH, S.E. 78 x 104. Line engraving by J. Cary after D. Parkes, 4 July 1800.
CRO

709. FLINT CHURCH. 200 x 365. Lithograph and soft ground etching by F.F. James and Sidney Massie, 1821.

710. FLINT CHURCH. 96 x 161. Lithograph by W. Green, Manchester, after F. de Tillegas. Published in W. Cathrall, *History of North Wales,* 1828.
CL

711. FLINT, The Old Parish Church in 1800, N.E. Prospect. 75 x 105. Line engraving by J. Cary after D. Parkes, 4 July 1800. Published in *The Gentleman's Magazine,* 1801.

712. FLINT, The Old Parish Church in 1800. 71 x 95. Etching [? by H. Beswick] after D. Parkes [cf. 711]. Published in H. Taylor, *Historic Notices of Flint,* 1883.
CRO*

713. FLINT, The New Parish Church, erected in 1848 on the Site of the Old Edifice. 85 x 90. Etching by H. Beswick. Published in H. Taylor, *Historic Notices of Flint,* 1883.
CRO*

714. FLINT, The Old Town Hall and Stocks. 160 x 95. Etching by Randolph Caldecott. Published in H. Taylor, *Historic Notices of Flint,* 1883.
CRO

715. [FLINT], The New Town Hall, erected on the site of the old building in 1840. 84 x 125. Etching by H. Beswick. Published in H. Taylor, *Historic Notices of Flint,* 1883.
CRO*

716. FLINT TOWN HALL & MARKET, View of. 315 x 447. Lithograph after F. Wehnert. Printed by Day & Haghe. John Welch, Architect. Dedicated to the Revd. William Maddock Williams.
CRO

717. GREDINGTON in Flintshire, The Seat of Lord Kenyon. 105 x 162. Line engraving by Walter Thomas after [W.] Evans. Published by Harrison & Co., 18 Paternoster Row, London, 1 August 1788. Also in *Picturesque Views of the Principal Seats of the Nobility*, 1787-8.
CRO

718. GREDINGTON in Flintshire, The Seat of Lord Kenyon. 97 x 160. Line engraving by Walter Thomas after [W.] Evans. (Variant of No. 717). Published by H.D. Symonds &c., 9 April 1796.

719. [GREENFIELD], River Bank Smelting Works. 114 x 153. Line engraving by J. Barlow after M. Griffith. Published in T. Pennant, *History of Whiteford and Holywell*, 1796.
CRO

720. GREENFIELD BRASS MILLS, near Holywell, Flintshire. 125 x 200. Line engraving by W.C. Wilson after J. Ingleby. Published by J. & J. Boydell, Cheapside & at the Shakspeare Gallery, Pall Mall, London, 25 June 1792. Also in R.C. Hoare, *Forty-Eight Views of Noblemen's and Gentlemen's Seats*, 1795.
CRO

721. GREENFIELD HALL, near Holywell, Flintshire. 129 x 182. Line engraving by W.C. Wilson after J. Ingleby. Published by J. & J. Boydell, No. 90 Cheapside, 25 March 1795. Also in R.C. Hoare, *Forty-Eight Views of Noblemen's and Gentlemen's Seats*, 1795.
CRO

722. GWERNHAYLOD. 144 x 221. Lithograph. Printed by C. Hullmandel. Published in H. Grueber, *Six Lithographic Views of Seats in the Neighbourhood of Wrexham, North Wales*.
CRO

723. GWYSANEY, Flintshire. 142 x 256. Photo-lithograph after M.E.P., 1862.
CRO

724. GYRN, Flintshire, East Front. 85 x 125. Line engraving by T. Jeavons after J.P. Neale. Published in J.P. Neale, *Views of the Seats of Noblemen*, 1818-23.
CRO

725. GYRN, Flintshire (Looking North East). 85 x 125. Line engraving by J. Barker after J.P. Neale. Published by J.P. Neale, 16 Bennett St., Blackfriars Road & Sherwood & Jones, Paternoster Row, 1 September 1824. Also in J.P. Neale, *Views of the Seats of Noblemen*, 1818-23.
CRO

726. HALKIN CASTLE, Flintshire. 257 x 385. Lithograph by W[illiam] Westall after J. [Chessel] Buckler. Printed by C. Hullmandel. Published by W. Clarke, New Bond Street, 1826.
CRO

727. [HANMER]. Ancient Cross and Yew-Trees in Hanmer Churchyard. 165 x 248. Lithograph. Published in J. Hanmer, *Memorial of the Parish of Hanmer in Flintshire*, 1872.
CRO*

728. HANMER HALL in Flintshire, The Seat of Mrs. Watson. 103 x 163. Line engraving by [J.] Walker after [W.] Evans. Published by Harrison & Co., 18 Paternoster Row, 1 March 1788. Also in *Picturesque Views of the Principal Seats of the Nobility*, 1787-8.
CRO

729. HANMER HALL in Flintshire, The Seat of Mrs. Watson. 97 x 160. Line engraving by [John] Walker after [William] Evans. Published by H.D. Symonds, No. 20 & Allen C. West No. 15 Paternoster Row & T. Conder, Bucklersbury, London, 23 April 1796.

730. HARRADEN CASTLE, North Wales. 105 x 159. Line engraving [by Alexander Hogg, 16 Paternoster Row, London].

731. HAWARDEN CASTLE. 85 x 129. Line engraving by H. [W.] Bond after J.P. Neale. Published in J.P. Neale, *Views of the Seats of Noblemen*, 1818-23.

732. HAWARDEN CASTLE. 108 x 165. Line engraving by W. Angus after M. Griffith. Published by White & Co., 1 May 1810. Also in T. Pennant, *Tours in Wales*, 1810. CRO

733. HAWARDEN CASTLE. 147 x 218. Soft ground etching by J.G. Wood. Published in J.G. Wood, *The Principal Rivers of Wales*, 1813. CRO

734. HAWARDEN CASTLE. 47 x 72. Line engraving. Published by T.T. & J. Tegg, Cheapside, 1 October 1832. Also in G.N. Wright, *Scenes in North Wales*, 1833. CRO*

735. HAWARDEN CASTLE. 136 x 195. Chromo-lithograph. Published in F.O. Morris, *Picturesque Views of Seats of the Noblemen, c.* 1880. CRO

736. HAWARDEN CASTLE. 130 x 185. Line engraving by C. Betrand from a photograph by permission of Messrs. Minshull & Hughes, Chester. Published by Cassell, Petter, Galpin & Co. in *Our Own Country*, Vol. V (1882).

737. HAWARDEN CASTLE. 145 x 223. Lithograph by Henry Grueber. Printed by Engelmann, Graf, Coindet & Co. Published in H. Grueber, *Six Lithographic Views of Seats in the Neighbourhood of Wrexham, North Wales*. CRO

738. HAWARDEN CASTLE. 67 x 71. Line engraving.

739. HAWARDEN CASTLE. 137 x 189. Lithograph.

740. HAWARDEN CASTLE in the County of Flint, The South East View of. 146 x 350. Line engraving by S. & N. Buck, 9 April 1742. Published in S. and N. Buck, *Views of all the Castles*, 1742. CRO

741. HAWARDEN CASTLE in the County of Flint, The South East View of. 72 x 136. Line engraving [after Buck]. Published in *A Description of England and Wales*, 1769 CRO

742. HAWARDEN CASTLE, Flintshire. 88 x 145. Line engraving by W[illiam] Radclyffe after H. Gastineau. Published by Jones & Co., Temple of the Muses, Finsbury Square, London, 1831. Also in *Wales Illustrated*, 1830. CRO

743. HAWARDEN CASTLE, Flintshire. 38 x 58. Line engraving.

744. HAWARDEN CASTLE, Flintshire [with account]. 104 x 152. Line engraving [by Richard] Godfrey, 1 July 1773. Published in F. Grose, *The Antiquities of England and Wales,* 1776.
CRO

745. HAWARDEN CASTLE, Flintshire, The Ruins of. The Property of Sir Stephen Richard Glynne, Bart., MP. 162 x 245. Lithograph by C.J. Greenwood.

746. [HAWARDEN], Lodge Gate - Broughton Approach. 90 x 138. Line engraving by Whymper. Published in *Hawarden Visitors' Hand-Book,* 1890.
CRO*

747. HAWARDEN CASTLE. 143 x 235. Line engraving by W. Watts after M. Griffith. Published in T. Pennant, *A Tour in Wales,* 1778.
CRO

748. HAWARDEN CASTLE. 84 x 118. Aquatint by G.J. Parkyns, 1 May 1793. Published in J. Moore & G.J. Parkyns, *Monastic Remains and Ancient Castles,* 1792.

749. HAWARDEN CASTLE in Flintshire. 78 x 102. Line engraving.
CRO

750. HAWARDEN CASTLE in Flintshire, A View of. 218 x 270. Line engraving by G. Barret. Published by J. Boydell, Cheapside, 1 March 1773.
CRO

751. HAWARDEN CASTLE in Flintshire, A View of Part of. 213 x 277. Line engraving by G. Barret. Published by J. Boydell, Cheapside, 1 March 1773.
CRO

752. [HAWARDEN CASTLE]. Gateway — Castle shewing Orphanage. 110 x 138. Line engraving by Whymper. Published in *Hawarden Visitors' Hand-Book,* 1890.
CRO*

753. [HAWARDEN CASTLE]. House and Flower Garden. 72 x 118. Line engraving by E. Johnson. Published in *Hawarden Visitors' Hand-Book,* 1890.
CRO*

754. [HAWARDEN CASTLE]. Ruins of Old Castle. 93 x 138. Line engraving by W.H. Published in *Hawarden Visitors' Hand-Book,* 1890.
CRO*

755. HAWARDEN CASTLE, The Seat of Sir S.R. Glynne, Bart., MP for the County of Flint. 230 x 283. Lithograph by W. Crane, Chester, after H.W. Unger.
CRO

756. HAWARDEN-CASTLE, in Flintshire, View of. 162 x 268. Line engraving [by W. Watts after M. Griffith]. Published in *The Modern Universal British Traveller,* 1779.
CRO

757. HAWARDEN CASTLE AND PARK in Flintshire, Five Miles from the City of Chester. The Seat of Sir John Glynne, Baronet. 399 x 556. Line engraving by Willm. Henry Toms after Thos. Badeslade, 1740.
CRO

758. HOWARD CASTLE, Flintshire. 104 x 152. Line engraving by [Richard] Godfrey, 1 July 1773. Published in F. Grose, *The Antiquities of England and Wales,* 1786.
CRO

759. HOWERDEN CASTLE, Flintshire. 104 x 152. Line engraving by [Richard] Godfrey, 1 July 1773. Published in F. Grose, *The Antiquities of England and Wales*, 1797.
CRO

760. HOWERDEN CASTLE. 91 x 65. Soft ground etching by B. Green.
CRO

761. HAWARDEN CHURCH, Flintshire. 106 x 148. Line engraving by J.H. Le Keux, *c.* 1860.
CRO

762. [HAWARDEN CHURCH]. Interior of Church. 93 x 138. Line engraving by W.H. Published in *Hawarden Visitors' Hand-Book*, 1890.
CRO*

763. HAWARDEN RECTORY, Flintshire. 1832. 156 x 235. Lithograph after Lady Charlotte Neville Grenville. Printed by W. Crane, Chester.
CRO

764. [HOLYWELL]. 123 x 185. Etching by G[eorge] Cuitt. Published in G. Cuitt, *Etchings of Ancient Buildings*, 1816, and *Wanderings and Pencillings*, 1855.
CRO*

765. [HOLYWELL]. Copper and Brass Works. 127 x 198. Line engraving by W. Angus after M. Griffith. Published by B. & J. White, 1 January 1796. Also in T. Pennant, *History of Whiteford and Holywell*, 1796.
CRO

766. [HOLYWELL]. Two Upper Cotton Works. 125 x 198. Line engraving by W. Angus after M. Griffith. Published by B. & J. White, 1 January 1796. Also in T. Pennant, *History of Whiteford and Holywell*, 1796.
CRO

767. HOLYWELL, Copper Works near, Belonging to the Mona Comp'y, Flintshire. 122 x 180. Line engraving by W. Watts after J. Ingleby. Published by J. & J. Boydell, Cheapside & at the Shakspeare Gallery, Pall Mall, 25 June 1792. Also in R.C. Hoare, *Forty-Eight Views of Noblemen's and Gentlemen's Seats*, 1795.
CRO

768. HOLYWELL, Cotton Works near, Belonging to Messrs. Douglas & Comp'y, Flintshire. 130 x 181. Line engraving by W.C. Wilson after J. Ingleby. Published by J. & J. Boydell, Cheapside & at the Shakspeare Gallery, Pall Mall, 25 June 1792. Also in R.C. Hoare, *Forty-Eight Views of Noblemen's and Gentlemen's Seats*, 1795.
CRO

769. HOLYWELL, Flintshire. Cotton Works near. 130 x 182. Line engraving by W. Watts after J. Ingleby. Published by J. & J. Boydell, Cheapside & at the Shakspeare Gallery, Pall Mall, 25 June 1792. Also in R.C. Hoare, *Forty-Eight Views of Noblemen's and Gentlemen's Seats*, 1795.
CRO

770. HOLYWELL, N.W., Pigsty at. 217 x 255. Etching by G. Cuitt, 1811. Published in G. Cuitt, *Etchings of Ancient Buildings*, 1816.
CRO*

771. HOLYWELL, N.W., Pigsty at. 86 x 59. Etching by G. Cuitt, 1815. Published in G. Cuitt, *Etchings of Ancient Buildings*, 1816.
CRO*

772. HOLYWELL, A View near. Four Views in Flintshire. Engraved by John Boydell, 1749. 195 x 283. Line engraving. Published by John Boydell at the Globe near Durham Yard in the Strand.
CRO

773. HOLYWELL, A View near. Four Views in Flintshire. Engraved by John Boydell, 1749. 195 x 283. Line engraving. Published by John Boydell at the Unicorn ye Corner of Queen Street, Cheapside, London, 1752. [cf. no. 772].
CRO

774. HOLYWELL CHURCH. 94 x 138. Line engraving by J. Le Keux after F. Mackenzie. Published by J.H. Parker, Oxford, C. Tilt, Fleet Street, London, and J. Le Keux, Harmondsworth, 1 February 1835.

775. HOLYWELL MILL (from Magdalen Walk). 67 x 115. Line engraving by Storer.

776. KINNERTON LODGE. 120 x 241. Lithograph by Evans & Gresty, Chester, after T.M. Penson.
CRO

777. LEESWOOD, Flintshire. The Seat of John Wynn Eyton, Esqr. 161 x 260. Lithograph by J. Shaw. Published by Henry Colburn, Great Marlborough Street. Printed by C.J. Greenwood, 1847.

778. LEESWOOD, The Gates of. 103 x 220. Aquatint by T. Cartwright after E. Pugh. Published by E. Williams, Strand, 15 August 1814. Also in E. Pugh, *Cambria Depicta,* 1816.
CRO

779. LLANERCH PANNA, near Ellesmere. Hon. Geo. T. Kenyon. John Douglas, Archt. 175 x 282. Lithograph. [Ground plan 32 x 89 bottom right].

780. LLWYN-EGRIN [Mold]. 113 x 184. Lithograph.
CRO

781. LLWYN-EGRIN [Mold]. 113 x 184. Lithograph. [Variant of No. 780, with figures in garden].

782. LLWYNEGRIN near Mold, Flintshire. A Seat of P. Davies Cooke, Esqr. Thomas Jones, Architect, Chester. 113 x 184. Lithograph by P. Gauci. Printed by Graf & Soret, 14 Newman St.

783. [LOGGERHEADS]. 101 x 150. Line engraving. Published in H.J. Tweddell, *Handy Guide to Mold and the Neighbourhood,* 1905.
CRO*

784. LOGGERHEADS, View near the. 144 x 196. Aquatint by T. Cartwright after E. Pugh. Published by E. Williams, Strand, 15 April 1813. Also in E. Pugh, *Cambria Depicta,* 1816.
CRO

785. MOEL FAMAU. 84 x 127. Wood engraving by H[ugh] Hughes. Published in H. Hughes, *The Beauties of Cambria,* 1823.
CRO*

786. MOEL FAMMA. 145 x 197. Aquatint by T. Cartwright after E. Pugh. Published by E. Williams, Strand, 15 December 1813. Also in E. Pugh, *Cambria Depicta,* 1816.
CRO

787. FOEL-FAMMA from Carreg Carn-March Arther. 224 x 302. Aquatint by W. Ellis after E. Pugh. Dedicated to Lord Bulkeley. Published by E. Pugh, Gt. Queen St., Lincoln's Inn Fields, 24 November 1794.
CRO

788. MOEL FAMMA. [Jubilee Monument]. 103 x 82. Line engraving. Published by Pring & Price [Mold]. Also in C.H. Leslie, *Rambles around Mold, c.* 1869.
CRO*

789. [MOEL FAMMA. Jubilee Monument]. 103 x 82. Line engraving. [cf. No. 788, retouched and Pring & Price imprint removed]. Published in H.J. Tweddell, *Handy Guide to Mold and the Neighbourhood,* 1905.
CRO*

790. [MOLD, Entrance to Leete and Moel Famau]. 102 x 151. Line engraving. Published in H.J. Tweddell, *Handy Guide to Mold and the Neighbourhood,* 1905.
CRO*

791. MOLD, Flintshire. 88 x 141. Line engraving by W. Wallis after H. Gastineau. Published in *Wales Illustrated,* 1830.
CRO

792. MOLD, Flintshire. 65 x 101. Line engraving [by Newman & Co.], *c.* 1860.

793. MOLD, Flintshire, The New Market Hall at. Alfred Lockwood, Archt. 185 x 266. Lithograph. Drawn by Philip C. Lockwood. Maclure, Macdonald & Macgregor, Lithographers, Liverpool, London & Manchester.
CRO

794. MOLD (From Argoed). 214 x 306. Lithograph. Published by Pring & Price, Mold.
CRO

795. [MOLD]. Hallelujah Monument. 134 x 104. Aquatint by T. Cartwright after E. Pugh. Published by E. Williams, Strand, 15 May 1814. Also in E. Pugh, *Cambria Depicta,* 1816.
CRO

796. [MOLD, High Street]. 100 x 149. Line engraving by Bourne. Published in H.J. Tweddell, *Handy Guide to Mold and the Neighbourhood,* 1905.
CRO*

797. MOLD, High Street. 67 x 100. Line engraving [by Newman & Co.].

798. [MOLD]. High Street (From the Cross). 214 x 303. Lithograph. Published by Pring & Price, Mold.
CRO

799. MOLD, Maesgarmon (The Bailey Hill and Church in the Distance). 77 x 110. Line engraving. Published by Pring & Price, Mold. Also in M.B. Clough, *Scenes and Stories Little Known,* 1861, and C.H. Leslie, *Rambles around Mold, c.* 1869.
CRO*

800. [MOLD, Maes Garmon]. 73 x 105. Line engraving. [cf. No. 799, retouched and Pring & Price imprint removed]. Published in H.J. Tweddell, *Handy Guide to Mold and the Neighbourhood,* 1905.
CRO*

801. MOLD, Riot at, June 2nd 1869 (Attack on the Military and Police at the Railway Station). 222 x 316. Lithograph by Pring & Price, Mold.
CRO

802. MOLD, Tower near. 126 x 99. Lithograph. Published in *Archaeologia Cambrensis,* 1846.
CRO*

803. MOLD, The Vale of. 140 x 198. Aquatint by T. Cartwright after E. Pugh. Published by E. Williams, Strand, 15 October 1813. Also in E. Pugh, *Cambria Depicta,* 1816.
CRO

804. MOLD CHURCH. 84 x 128. Wood engraving by H. Hughes. Published in H. Hughes, *The Beauties of Cambria,* 1823.
CRO*

805. MOLD, Interior of St. Mary's Church. 82 x 74. Line engraving by Newman & Co., 48 Watling St., London.

806. MOLD, St. Mary's Church, N.E. 75 x 114. Line engraving. Published by Pring & Price, Mold. Also in M.B. Clough, *Scenes and Stories Little Known,* 1861, and C.H. Leslie, *Rambles around Mold, c.* 1869.
CRO*

807. MOLD, St. Mary's Church. 107 x 142. Photo-lithograph by Whiteman & Bass, London. Published in D.R. Thomas, *History of the Diocese of St. Asaph,* 1874.
CRO*

808. [MOLD, St. Mary's Church]. 75 x 114. Line engraving. [cf. No. 806, retouched and Pring & Price imprint removed]. Published in H.J. Tweddell, *Handy Guide to Mold and the Neighbourhood,* 1905.
CRO*

809. MOLD, St. Mary's Church. [South View]. 68 x 99. Line engraving by Newman & Co., 48 Watling St., London.

810. MOLD, St. Mary's Parish Church. [S.W. View]. 272 x 246. Lithograph. Published by Pring & Price, Mold.
CRO

811. MOLD, St. Mary's Parish Church. [Interior, nave, looking east]. 272 x 250. Lithograph. Published by Pring & Price, Mold.
CRO

812. MOLD CHURCH AND NATIONAL SCHOOLS, View of. 246 x 312. Lithograph. Printed by C. Moody, Holborn. Published by J. Price, Bookseller, Mold, *c.* 1838.
CRO

813. [MOSTYN HALL]. 162 x 236. Lithograph.
CRO

814. [MOSTYN HALL]. 162 x 236. Lithograph.
CRO

815. MOSTYN. 41 x 67. Line engraving. Published by T.T. & J. Tegg, Cheapside, 1 October 1832. Also in G.N. Wright, *Scenes in North Wales,* 1833.
CRO*

816. MOSTYN, Antient Water Wheel near. 119 diam. Line engraving after Thomas Dineley's sketch in *Duke of Beaufort's Progress,* 1684. Published in T. Pennant, *History of Whiteford and Holywell,* 1796.
CRO*

817. MOSTYN as in 1684. 118 diam. Line engraving after Thomas Dineley's sketch in *Duke of Beaufort's Progress,* 1684. Published by B. & J. White, 1 January 1796. Also in T. Pennant, *History of Whiteford and Holywell,* 1796.
CRO*

818. MOSTYN, Front of, 1631. 68 x 94. Line engraving [by J. Barlow after M. Griffith]. Published by B. & J. White, 1 January 1796. Also in T. Pennant, *History of Whiteford and Holywell,* 1796.
CRO*

819. MOSTYN, Flintshire. The Seat of the Honble Edward Mostyn Lloyd Mostyn, MP. 162 x 248. Lithograph by C.J. Greenwood after J. Shaw.

820. MOSTYN HALL, Flintshire. The Seat of Sir Roger Mostyn, Bart. 130 x 182. Line engraving by W.C. Wilson after M. Griffith. Published by J. & J. Boydell, Cheapside, & at the Shakspeare Gallery, Pall Mall, 25 June 1792. Also in R.C. Hoare, *Forty-Eight Views of Noblemen's and Gentlemen's Seats,* 1795.
CRO

821. MOSTYN HALL. 111 x 184. Line engraving by J. Barlow after M. Griffith, 1795. Published by B. & J. White, 1 January 1796. Also in T. Pennant, *History of Whiteford and Holywell,* 1796.
CRO

822. NANERTH ROCKS. 115 x 159. Aquatint after S. Ireland.

823. NANNERCH, Flintshire. Perspective View of Proposed New Church at. T.H.Wyatt, Architect. 205 x 236. Lithograph by S. Salter Junr. Printed by Day & Son, *c.* 1853.
CRO

824. NANT-Y-FRIDD FALL. 141 x 195. Aquatint by T. Bonnor after E. Pugh. Published by E. Williams, Strand, 15 July 1813. Also in E. Pugh, *Cambria Depicta,* 1816.
CRO

825. NORTHOP, Flintshire. 90 x 147. Line engraving by S. Lacey after H. Gastineau. Published by Jones & Co., Temple of the Muses, Finsbury Square, London, 1831. Also in *Wales Illustrated,* 1830.
CRO

826. NORTHOP, Flintshire. St. Peter's Church. 219 x 178. Photo-lithograph by Whiteman & Bass. John Douglas, Architect.
CRO

827. NORTHOP CHURCH, as it appeared August 1839. 342 x 260. Lithograph by G. Hawkins from a sketch by Edward Falkener, architect, 6 Arthur Street, London. Published by Day & Haghe, lithographers.
CRO

828. NORTHOP CHURCH, Flintshire. W. Elevation of Tower. 438 x 275. Lithograph by G.S. after A.S. Published by A. Macgregor (late Maclure, Macdonald & Macgregor), Liverpool & Manchester.
CRO

829. OVERTON BRIDGE, Over the river Dee on the confines of Denbigh and Flintshire. 208 x 292. Aquatint by Paul Sandby. Published by P. Sandby, St. Georges Row, 1 September 1776. Also in P. Sandby, *Twelve Views in North Wales,* 1776.
CRO

830. OVERTON BRIDGE, View of. 307 x 430. Aquatint by F. Jukes after T. Walmsley. Dedicated to Charles Browne, Esqr. Published by T. Jukes, 10 Howland St., London, 12 June 1794. Also in T. Walmsley & F. Jukes, *Views in North Wales,* 1792-4.

831. OVERTON CHURCH, Flintshire. 90 x 145. Line engraving by W. Radclyffe after H. Gastineau. Published in *Wales Illustrated*, 1830.
CRO

832. PENGWERN. 108 x 164. Aquatint [by J. Bluck after J.C. Ibbetson]. Published in J. Baker, *A Picturesque Guide through Wales and the Marches*, 1795.
CRO

833. PENGWERN PLACE, Flintshire. 83 x 124. Line engraving by T. Matthews after J.P. Neale. Published by W.H. Reid, 32 Whitehall, 1 June 1818. Also in J.P. Neale, *Views of the Seats of Noblemen*, 1818-23.
CRO

834. PENLEY CHAPEL & NATIONAL SCHOOL. 67 x 110. Lithograph.
CRO

835. PENLEY CHURCH. 158 x 212. Aquatint by G. Hunt after D. Cox. Published by T. Clay, 18 Ludgate Hill, London, May 1823. Also in D. Cox, *A Series of Progressive Lessons*, 1823.

836. PENTRE HOBIN, Flintshire. 173 x 248. Photo-lithograph after M.E.P., 1862.
CRO

837. PENTRE-HOBIN, Flintshire. The Seat of Thomas Trevor Mather, Esqr. 164 x 246. Lithograph by J. Shaw. Printed by Henry Colburn, Great Marlborough Street, 1847.

838. PLAS TEG, The Seat of T.B. Trevor Roper, Esqr. 235 x 374. Lithograph.

839. POINT OF AIR, Flintshire, The Lighthouse on. 196 x 238. Aquatint by William Daniell. Published by Messrs. Longman & Co., Paternoster Row & W. Daniell, 9 Cleveland St., Fitzroy Square, 1 July 1815. Also in W. Daniell, *A Voyage Round Great Britain*, 1815.
CRO

840. PONT NEWITH near St. Asaph. 187 x 263. Aquatint by [John] Hill after [T.] Walmesley. Published by John Murphy, 19 Howland St., Fitzroy Square & at G. Testolines, 73 Cornhill, 25 June 1810.
CRO

841. PONTRIFFITH, Flintshire. The Seat of Llewelyn Lloyd, Esqr. 163 x 245. Lithograph by J. Shaw. Printed by C.J. Greenwood.

842. RHUAL, The Seat of Fred. C. Philips, Esqr. 337 x 409. Lithograph by W. Crane, Chester.
CRO

843. RHIDLAND, Flintshire. 180 x 246. Etching by F. Stevens after J. Varley. Published by R. Ackermann, 101 Strand, 1 May 1815. Also in F. Stevens, *Views of Cottages and Farmhouses in England and Wales*, 1815.
CRO

844. RUDDLAN. 150 x 224. Soft ground etching by J.G. Wood. Published in J.G. Wood, *The Principal Rivers of Wales*, 1813.
CRO

845. RUDLAND. 84 x 118 diam. Line engraving. Published in T. Pennant, *Journey to Snowdon*, 1781, and *A Tour in Wales*, 1784.
CRO*

846. RUTHLAN. 128 x 189. Line engraving by W. Byrne after R.C. Hoare. Published by William Miller, Albemarle Street, London, 1 March 1806. Also in R.C. Hoare, *Forty-Eight Views of Noblemen's and Gentlemen's Seats*, 1795.
CRO

847. RHUDDLAN CASTLE. 73 x 102. Line engraving. Published in A. Batenham, *Traveller's Companion . . . from Chester through North Wales*, 1825.
CRO*

848. RHUDDLAN CASTLE. 42 x 72. Line engraving. Published by T.T. & J. Tegg, Cheapside, 1 October 1832. Also in G.N. Wright, *Scenes in North Wales*, 1833.
CRO*

849. RHUDDLAN CASTLE. 42 x 60. Line engraving by Newman & Co., London.

850. RHUDDLAN CASTLE. 95 x 170. Line engraving by W.H. Lizars. Published by Thomas Catherall, Chester.
CRO

851. RHUDDLAN CASTLE, 186 x 277. Lithograph by G. Hawkins after G. Pickering. Printed by Day & Son. Published by Prichard & Roberts, Bridge St. Row, Chester.
CRO

852. RHUDDLAN CASTLE. 186 x 276. Lithograph by G. Hawkins after G. Pickering. Printed by Day & Son. Published by George Prichard, Bridge St. Row, Chester.

853. RHUDDLAN CASTLE. 50 x 80. Line engraving by T. Gilks.

854. RHUDDLAN CASTLE. 62 x 191. Line engraving by Newman & Co.

855. RHUDDLAN CASTLE in the County of Flint, The South West View of. 148 x 351. Line engraving by S. and N. Buck, 9 April 1742. Published in S. and N. Buck, *Views of all the Castles*, 1742.
CRO

856. RHUDDLAN CASTLE, Daguerreotype View of. 75 x 105. Line engraving. Published by W.L. Sharp, Rhyl, artist.

857. RHUDDLAN CASTLE erected by Edward 1st. 225 x 317. Lithograph by Newman & Co., 48 Watling Street, London. Published by D.Ll. Lewis, Rhyl, *c.* 1852.
CRO

858. RHUDDLAN CASTLE, Flintshire. 89 x 143. Line engraving by H. Adlard after H. Gastineau. Published in *Wales Illustrated*, 1830.
CRO

859. RHUDDLAN CASTLE, Flintshire, Interior of. 98 x 154. Line engraving by Newman & Co. Published by D.Ll. Lewis, Rhyl, *c.* 1852.
CRO

860. RHUDDLAN CASTLE, Flintshire. 90 x 159. Lithograph by C. Lawrie after W. Simpson. Published by Blackie & Son, London, Glasgow & Edinburgh. Also in O. Jones, *Cymru: Yn Hanesyddol, Parthedegol a Bywgraphyddol*, cyf. II, 1875.
CRO

861. RHUDDLAN CASTLE in Flintshire, A North West View of. 274 x 434. Line engraving by John Boydell. Published by J. Boydell, 1749.
CRO

862. RHUDDLAN CASTLE near Rhyl. 50 x 80. Line engraving. Published by [H.] Humphreys, Carnarvon.

863. RHUDDLAN CASTLE near Rhyl, Flintshire. 100 x 160. Line engraving by Newman & Co. Published by E. Powell Jones, Chymist, Rhyl.

864. RHUDDLAN CASTLE, South West View of. 108 x 176. Photo-lithograph, 1882.

865. RHUDLAN CASTLE. 82 x 125. Line engraving by Metcalf [after Buck] *c.* 1760.
CRO

866. RHUDLAN CASTLE. 82 x 125. Line engraving by J. Ryland after B. Ralph. Published in *England Illustrated,* 1764.
CRO

867. RHUDLAN CASTLE in the County of Flint, The South West View of. 74 x 140. Line engraving. Published in *A Description of England and Wales,* 1769.

868. RHUDLAN CASTLE, in Flintshire. 80 x 100. Line engraving. [Published by Alexander Hogg, 16 Paternoster Row, London].
CRO

869. RHUDLAND CASTLE, Flintshire [with account]. 102 x 146. Line engraving by S. Sparrow, 11 August 1773. Published in F. Grose, *The Antiquities of England and Wales,* 1776.
CRO

870. RHUDLAND CASTLE in Flintshire. 123 x 182. Line engraving by Hawkins. Published by Alexander Hogg, 16 Paternoster Row, London.
CRO

871. RHYDDLAN CASTLE. 62 x 92. Line engraving by E. Finden after Capt. R[obert] Batty. Published by John Murray, London, 1 August 1823. Also in R. Batty, *Welsh Scenery,* 1823.
CRO

872. RHYDDLAN CASTLE. 62 x 95. Line engraving by Newman & Co. Published in W. Davis, *Hand-Book for the Vale of Clwyd,* 1856.
CRO*

873. RHYDDLAN CASTLE, Flintshire. 61 x 85. Line engraving by Rock & Co., 1 December 1855.
CRO

874. RUTHLAN CASTLE in the County of Denbigh [sic]. 202 x 300. Line engraving by James Peak after W. Williams. Published by J. Wesson, Litchfield Street, Soho.
CRO

875. CASTELL RHUDDLAN. 96 x 150. Line engraving by W. Radclyffe after J. Wrightson, *c.* 1836.

876. RHUDDLAN CASTLE AND MARSHES. 137 x 198. Line engraving by Whymper. Published in *Our Own Country,* Vol. 5, 1882.

877. RHUDDLAN CASTLE AND RIVER CLWYD. 95 x 149. Line engraving by W. Radclyffe after J. Wrightson. Published in T. Roscoe, *Wanderings and Excursions in North Wales,* 1836.
CRO*

878. RHUDDLAN CASTLE AND RIVER CLWYD. 88 x 139. Line engraving by W. Radclyffe. Published in W. Cathrall, *Wanderings in North Wales*, 1851.
CL

879. RUDLAND CASTLE, CHURCH, BRIDGE & HARBOUR, Flintshire, A Distant View of. 127 x 178. Line engraving by W.C. Wilson after M. Griffith. Published by J. & J. Boydell, No. 90 Cheapside & at the Shakspeare Gallery, Pall Mall, 25 March 1795. Also in R.C. Hoare, *Forty-Eight Views of Noblemen's and Gentlemen's Seats*, 1795.
CRO

880. RHUDDLAN CHURCH, CASTLE, &c. 84 x 128. Wood engraving by H. Hughes. Published in H. Hughes, *The Beauties of Cambria*, 1823.
CRO*

881. RHUDDLAN PRIORY, in the County of Flint, The South East View of. 145 x 348. Line engraving by S. and N. Buck, 9 April 1742. Dedicated to Robert Davies Esqr. Published in S. and N. Buck, *Views of all the Castles*, 1742.
CRO

882. RHYL. 75 x 134. Line engraving. Published by Thomas Catherall, Chester. Also in E. Parry, *The Cambrian Mirror*, 1850.

883. RHYL. 57 x 90. Line engraving by Rock & Co., 25 January 1869. Published in *The Queen's Album of North Wales*.

884. RHYL. 75 x 90. Line engraving by Newman & Co., 48 Watling St., London.

885. [RHYL]. 84 x 146. Lithograph by . . . Coley, Rogers . . . Published by D. Ll. Lewis.
CRO

886. RHYL. 90 x 170. Line engraving by W.H. Lizars. Published by Thomas Catherall, Chester.
CRO

887. RHYL. 95 x 175. Line engraving. Published by T. Catherall, Chester.

888. RHYL. 100 x 170. Line engraving by W. Banks & Son, Edinburgh. Published by T. Catherall, Chester. Also in T. Catherall, *Views in North Wales, c.* 1860.
CL

889. [RHYL]. The Church intended to be erected at Rhyl in the County of Flint to contain 204 private and 223 unappropriated sittings. Thos. Jones, Architect. 100 x 180. Lithograph by Paul Gauci, *c.* 1833. [Trinity Church, built 1835].
CRO

890. RHYL, Flintshire (looking West from the Pier). 63 x 92. Line engraving by Rock & Co., 25 January 1869. Published in Rock & Co., *Picturesque Views in North Wales*, 1871.

891. RHYL, From the Sea. 80 x 110. Line engraving by W.L. Sharp, Artist, Rhyl.

892. RHYL, Looking East. 80 x 115. Line engraving by W. Banks & Son, Edinburgh. Published by Catherall & Prichard, Chester. Also in T. Catherall, *Views in North Wales, c.* 1860.
CRO

893. RHYL, Looking East. 184 x 298. Lithograph. Printed by Day & Son. Published by Catherall & Prichard, Chester.
CRO

894. RHYL, Looking West. 80 x 115. Line engraving by W. Banks & Son, Edinburgh. Published by Catherall & Prichard, Chester. Also in T. Catherall, *Views in North Wales, c.* 1860.
CRO

895. RHYL, Looking West. 187 x 296. Lithograph. Printed by Day & Son. Published by Catherall & Prichard, Chester.
CRO

896. RHYL, Looking West. 186 x 297. Lithograph by Day & Son. Published by H. Humphreys, Castle Square, Carnarvon.

897. RHYL, North Wales. 65 x 92. Line engraving by Newman & Co. Published in W. Davis, *Hand-Book for the Vale of Clwyd,* 1856.
CRO

898. RHYL, North Wales. 68 x 95. Line engraving by Rock & Co., London, 16 March 1863.

899. RHYL, North Wales. 52 x 79. Line engraving. Engraved and printed by H. Humphreys, Carnarvon.

900. RHYL, North Wales. 64 x 92. Line engraving by Newman & Co. Published by D. Ll. Lewis, Rhyl.

901. RHYL, North Wales. 100 x 152. Line engraving by Newman & Co. Published by D.Ll. Lewis, Rhyl, North Wales.
CRO

902. RHYL, North Wales. 200 x 284. Lithograph by Newman & Co. Published by D.Ll. Lewes, Rhyl.
CRO

903. RHYL, North Wales, 218 x 325. Lithograph by Newman & Co. Published by D.Ll. Lewis, Rhyl.
CRO

904. RHYL, North Wales. 82 x 115. Line engraving. Published by B. Lewis, Stationer, Rhyl.

905. RHYL, North Wales. 125 x 328. Lithograph by E.H. Buckler. Printed by C. Moody, 257 Holborn. Published by D. Ll. Lewis, Stationer, Water Street, Rhyl, North Wales.

906. RHYL, North Wales. 220 x 322. Lithograph by Newman & Co. Published by E.P. Jones, Chemist, Rhyl.

907. RHYL, North Wales, From the Sea. 68 x 95. Line engraving by Newman & Co., 48 Watling Street, London, July 1869.

908. RHYL, Flintshire, The Pier. 64 x 95. Line engraving by Rock & Co., 1 January 1868.

909. RHYL, The New Pier. 60 x 95. Line engraving by Newman & Co., 48 Watling St., London, September 1868.
CRO

910. RHYL, Flintshire, St. Thomas' Church. 62 x 92. Line engraving by Rock & Co. Published 1 January 1868.

911. RHYL, The New Church of St. Thomas. 120 x 110. Lithograph. Printed by J. Dayton Wyatt, *c.* 1870.

912. RHYL, St. Thomas's Church. 223 x 290. Lithograph. Published by D.Ll. Lewis, Rhyl, *c.* 1870. [This church was built 1861-9].

913. RHYLLON, near St. Asaph. 75 x 90. Line engraving by J.H. Kernot after Mrs. Hemans. Published by William Blackwood & Sons, Edinburgh & London. Also in *The Poems of Felicia Hemans,* 1859.
CRO

914. RHYLLON, near St. Asaph. The Residence of Mrs. Hemans. 80 x 115. Line engraving by W. Greathatch. Published by Saunders & Otley, Conduit St., London.
CRO

915. ST. ASAPH. 52 x 83. Etching by John Musgrove, 1810.

916. ST. ASAPH. 156 x 231. Soft ground etching by J.G. Wood. Published in J.G. Wood, *The Principal Rivers of Wales,* 1813.
CRO

917. ST. ASAPH. 155 x 239. Aquatint by T. Fielding after C.V. Fielding. Published by T. Clay, 18 Ludgate Hill, London, 1 May 1820. Also in T. Compton, *The Northern Cambrian Mountains,* 1820.

918. ST. ASAPH. 152 x 240. Aquatint by S. Prout, 1 February 1836. Published in T. Compton, *The Northern Cambrian Mountains,* 1820.

919. ST. ASAPH. 44 x 71. Line engraving. Published in T. Evans, *Walks Through Wales,* 1819, and G.A. Cooke, *Topographical and Statistical Description of Wales, c.* 1830.

920. ST. ASAPH. 42 x 67. Line engraving. Published by T.T. & J. Tegg, Cheapside, 1 October 1832. Also in G.N. Wright, *Scenes in North Wales,* 1833.
CRO*

921. ST. ASAPH. 95 x 147. Line engraving by W. Radclyffe after J. Wrightson. Published in T. Roscoe, *Wanderings and Excursions in North Wales,* 1836.
CRO

922. ST. ASAPH. 60 x 86. Line engraving by Newman & Co., Watling St., London. Published in W. Davis, *Hand-Book for the Vale of Clwyd,* 1856.
CRO*

923. ST. ASAPH. 71 x 119. Line engraving by S. Lacey. Published by J. Mason, 14 City Road, and at 16 Paternoster Row.

924. ST. ASAPH. 98 x 170. Line engraving. Published by T. Catherall, Chester. Also in T. Catherall, *Views in North Wales, c.*1860.
CRO

925. [ST. ASAPH]. 77 x 121. Line engraving.
CRO

926. ST. ASAPH. 40 x 70. Line engraving by T. Gilks.

927. ST. ASAPH. 43 x 71. Line engraving.
CRO

928. ST. ASAPH, by the Welch called Llan Elwy ... 340 x 778. Line engraving by J. Lewis. Dedicated to the Honble Robt. Davis of Llannerch, Esqr.

929. ST. ASAPH, LLANELWY, The City of. 143 x 227. Lithograph by Newman & Co., 48 Watling St., London.
CRO

930. LANELWY. ST. ASAPH. 129 x 190. Line engraving by W. Byrne after R.C. Hoare. Published by William Miller, Albemarle Street, London, 1 March 1806. Published in R.C. Hoare, *Forty-Eight Views of Noblemen's and Gentlemen's Seats*, 1795.
CRO

931. ST. ASAPH'S [sic], The Bishop's Palace. 76 x 118. Line engraving by H.S. Storer. Published by Sherwood, Neely & Jones, Paternoster Row, 1 January 1818. Also in J.N. Brewer, *History and Antiquities of the Cathedral Church of St. Asaph,* 1819.
CRO

932. ST. ASAPH, Bridge over the River Clwyd near. 65 x 88. Line engraving by J.H. Kernot after T.C. Dibdin and F. Hemans. Published in *The Poems of Felicia Hemans,* 1859.

933. ST. ASAPH, Bronwylfa. 175 x 277. Photo-lithograph. Printed by James Akerman, 6 Queen Square W.C. John Douglas, Architect.
CRO

934. ST. ASAPH in the County of Flint, The South East View of the Church & Palace of. 148 x 350. Line engraving by S. and N. Buck, 9 April 1742. Dedicated to Isaac, Lord Bishop of St.Asaph. Published in S. and N. Buck, *Views of all the Castles,* 1742.
CRO

935. ST. ASAPH, The Deanery House, N.E. View of. Thomas Jones, Architect, Chester. 113 x 186. Lithograph by Paul Gauci. Published by Engelmann & Co.
CRO

936. ST. ASAPH, The Deanery House, S.E. View of. Thomas Jones, Architect, Chester. 113 x 186. Lithograph by Paul Gauci. Published by Engelmann & Co.
CRO

937. ST. ASAPH, Flintshire. 115 x 200. Lithograph by Engelmann & Co. after W. Nield, Chester. Published in W. Cathrall, *History of North Wales,* 1828.
CL

938. ST. ASAPH, Flintshire. 91 x 149. Line engraving by H.S. Storer after H. Gastineau. Published in *Wales Illustrated,* 1830.
CRO

939. ST. ASAPH in Flintshire, North Wales, View of the Cathedral Church of. 90 x 161. Line engraving by Thornton. Published by Alexander Hogg, 16 Paternoster Row.
CRO

940. ST. ASAPH, North Wales. 66 x 95. Line engraving by Rock & Co., London, 16 March 1863.

941. ST. ASAPH, Our Lady's Well near. 67 x 84. Line engraving by J.H. Kernot after F. Hemans. Published in *The Poems of Felicia Hemans*, 1859.

942. ST. ASAPH, The Cathedral Church of. 428 x 570. Line engraving. Printed and sold by J. Smith in Exeter Change in ye Strand, [1710].
CRO

943. ST. ASAPH, The Cathedral Church of. 138 x 183. Line engraving by J. Harris, *c.* 1760.
CRO

944. ST. ASAPH [CATHEDRAL]. 52 x 83. Etching by John Musgrove, 1810.

945. ST. ASAPH CATHEDRAL. 84 x 128. Wood engraving by H. Hughes. Published in H. Hughes, *The Beauties of Cambria*, 1823.
CRO*

946. ST. ASAPH'S CATHEDRAL. 145 x 205. Line engraving by John and Charles Walker after J. Jones. [From C. & J. Greenwood's map of Flintshire, Denbighshire and Montgomeryshire, 1834].

947. ST. ASAPH [CATHEDRAL]. 67 x 98. Line engraving.

948. ST. ASAPH [CATHEDRAL]. 77 x 115. Line engraving.

949. ST. ASAPH [CATHEDRAL]. The Bishoprick of St. Asaph contains part of the counties of Denbigh, Flint, Montgomery, Merioneth & some towns in Shropshire . . . 123 x 120. Line engraving.

950. ST. ASAPH, CATHEDRAL OF. 138 x 208. Line engraving/etching by Kronheim & Co., London.
CRO

951. ST. ASAPH CATHEDRAL. 285 x 224. Lithograph. Published by C. Story.
CRO

952. ST. ASAPH'S CATHEDRAL, Choir of. 110 x 86. Line engraving by H.S. Storer. Dedicated to the Rt. Rev. John Luxmore, DD, & FSA, Lord Bishop of St. Asaph. Published by Sherwood, Neely & Jones, Paternoster Row, 1 January 1818. Also in J.N. Brewer, *History and Antiquities of the Cathedral Church of St. Asaph*, 1819.
CRO

953. ST. ASAPH'S CATHEDRAL, The Choir. 137 x 108. Line engraving by B. Winkles after C. Warren and B. Baud. Published in T. Moule, *Winkle's Cathedrals of England and Wales*, 1842.
CRO

954. ST. ASAPH'S CATHEDRAL, East End. 79 x 113. Line engraving by J. Storer. Published by Sherwood, Neely & Jones, Paternoster Row, 1 January 1818. Also in J.N. Brewer, *History and Antiquities of the Cathedral Church of St. Asaph*, 1819.
CRO

955. ST. ASAPH CATHEDRAL, Flintshire. 89 x 145. Line engraving by H.S. Storer after H. Gastineau. Published in *Wales Illustrated*, 1830.
CRO

956. ST. ASAPH'S CATHEDRAL, Nave of. 106 x 87. Line engraving by J. Storer. Published by Sherwood, Neely & Jones, Paternoster Row, 1 January 1818. Also in J.N. Brewer, *History and Antiquities of the Cathedral Church of St. Asaph*, 1819.
CRO

957. ST. ASAPH'S CATHEDRAL, North Trancept. 111 x 87. Line engraving by J.Storer. Published by Sherwood, Neely & Jones, Paternoster Row, 1 January 1818. Also in J.N. Brewer, *History and Antiquities of the Cathedral Church of St. Asaph*, 1819.
CRO

958. ST. ASAPH CATHEDRAL, N.W. 163 x 250. Line engraving by J. C[hessel] Buckler. Published by J.C. Buckler, Bermondsey, Surrey, 1 June 1820.
CRO

959. ST. ASAPH, The South Prospect of the Cathedral Church of. Sti. Asaphensis: Eccl: Cath : facies Australis. 170 x 284. Line engraving by Daniel King after Randoll Holme, junior. Published in D. King, *Cathedrall & Conventuall Churches of England and Wales*, 1656.
CRO

960. ST. ASAPH CATHEDRAL, South Prospect. 165 x 265. Line engraving by J. Harris after Joseph Lord. Published in Browne Willis, *A Survey of the Cathedral Church of St. Asaph*, 1720.
CRO*

961. ST. ASAPH'S CATHEDRAL, S.E. View. 80 x 114. Line engraving by H.S. Storer. Published by Sherwood, Neely & Jones, 1 January 1818.
CRO

962. ST. ASAPH'S CATHEDRAL, S.W. View of. 77 x 121. Line engraving by H.S. Storer. Published in J.N. Brewer, *History and Antiquities of the Cathedral Church of St. Asaph*, 1819.

963. ST. ASAPH CATHEDRAL from the South West. 95 x 155. Photo-lithograph from a photograph by F. Bedford. Published in D.R. Thomas, *History of the Diocese of St. Asaph*, 1874.
CRO*

964. ST. ASAPH'S CATHEDRAL, View from the Bridge. 104 x 142. Line engraving by B. Winkles after C. Warren and B. Baud. Published in T. Moule, *Winkle's Cathedrals of England and Wales*, 1842.
CRO

965. ST. ASAPH, View of the Cathedral Church of. 90 x 162. Line engraving by Thornton. Published by Alexander Hogg, 16 Paternoster Row.

966. ST. ASAPH'S CATHEDRAL, West End of. 78 x 117. Line engraving by H.S. Storer. Published by Sherwood, Neely & Jones, Paternoster Row, 1 December 1817. Also in J.N. Brewer, *History and Antiquities of the Cathedral Church of St.Asaph*, 1819.
CRO

967. ST. ASAPH'S CATHEDRAL, West End. 110 x 142. Line engraving by B. Winkles after C. Warren. Published in T. Moule, *Winkle's Cathedrals of England and Wales*, 1842.
CRO

968. ST. ASAPH CATHEDRAL, CHURCH & BRIDGE. 105 x 150. Line engraving by [S.] Sparrow after S. Hooper, 12 March 1786. Published in F. Grose, *The Antiquities of England and Wales*, 1786.
CRO

969. ST. WENEFREDE'S CHAPEL. 100 x 169. Line engraving after David Parkes, 1800. Published in *The Gentleman's Magazine*, 1804.
CRO

970. ST. WINIFRED'S CHAPEL & ST. MARY'S CHURCH. 65 x 81. Line engraving by Rock & Co., London, 18 October 1855.

971. ST. WINFFRID'S WELL. 110 x 120. Line engraving. [From John Speed's map of Flintshire, 1611].
CRO

972. ST. WINEFRID'S WELL. 110 diam. Line engraving by J. Ryland after B. Ralph. Published in *England and Wales Illustrated*, 1764.
CRO

973. ST. WINIFRED'S WELL. 170 x 264. Line engraving. Published in *England Displayed*, 1769.
CRO

974. ST. WINEFRED'S WELL. 106 x 151. Line engraving by [S.] Sparrow after S. Hooper, 24 May 1788. Published in F. Grose, *The Antiquities of England and Wales*, 1797.
CRO

975. ST. WINEFRID'S WELL. 105 x 132. Aquatint by J. Havell after E. Pugh. Published by E. Williams, Strand, 15 November 1814. Also in E. Pugh, *Cambria Depicta*, 1816.
CRO

976. ST. WINIFREDS WELL. 42 x 71. Line engraving. Published by T.T. & J. Tegg, Cheapside, 1 October 1832. Also in G.N. Wright, *Scenes in North Wales*, 1833.
CRO*

977. ST. WINEFRED'S WELL. 180 x 253. Lithograph by W. Crane, Chester, after H. Hughes. Published by James Davies, High St., Holywell, 1839.
CRO

978. [ST. WINEFRIDE'S WELL]. 336 x 474. Lithograph by J.A. Mulligan. Published by J.A. Mulligan, Rhyl. Vincent Brooks, Day & Son, lithographers, 10 October 1896.

979. [ST. WINEFRIDE'S WELL]. 125 x 180. Line engraving by P. Mazell after J. Gresse.

980. ST. WINEFRID'S WELL. 97 x 104. Line engraving by Metcalf.
CRO

981. ST. WINEFRED'S WELL. 98 x 154. Line engraving.
CRO

982. ST. WINIFRID'S WELL. 100 x 161. Line engraving.
CRO

983. ST. WINEFRED'S WELL. 181 x 254. Lithograph by Hugh Hughes.

984. ST. WINIFRID'S WELL, Flintshire [with account]. 103 x 151. Line engraving by B. Godfrey, 20 March 1772. Published in F. Grose, *The Antiquities of England and Wales*, 1776.
CRO

985. ST. WINEFRED'S WELL, Flintshire. 104 x 152. Line engraving by B. Godfrey, 20 March 1786. Published in F. Grose, *The Antiquities of England and Wales*, 1786. [Retouched version of No. 984].

986. ST. WINIFRED'S WELL. 72 x 103. Line engraving. Published by G. Robinson & Co., March 1789. Also in *Ladies Magazine.*
CRO

987. ST. WINIFRED'S WELL, Flintshire. 152 x 98. Line engraving by W. Wallis after H. Gastineau. Published in *Wales Illustrated,* 1830.
CRO

988. ST. WINIFRED'S WELL, Flintshire, North Wales, Inside View of. 170 x 102. Line engraving by [W.] Angus. Published by R.N. Rose, 45 Holborn Hill, 1 May 1820.

989. ST. WINEFREDE'S WELL, Flintshire, An Outside View of. 83 x 140. Woodcut.

990. ST. WINIFRID'S WELL, Flintshire, North Wales. 74 x 96. Line engraving by Jones & Co., 22 March 1825. Published in *The New Wonderful and Entertaining Magazine,* Vol. 1, 1827.

991. ST. WINIFRED'S WELL, Flintshire, North Wales, An Inside View of. 283 x 355. Line engraving by John Ingleby, 1 January 1781. Published by E. Carnes, Holywell.
CRO

992. ST. WINIFRID'S WELL in Flintshire. 79 x 98. Line engraving. Published by Alexander Hogg, 16 Paternoster Row.
CRO

993. ST. WINIFRID'S WELL in Flintshire. 124 x 185. Line engraving by Hawkins. Published by Alexander Hogg, 16 Paternoster Row.
CRO

994. [ST. WINIFRED'S WELL], Holywell. 52 x 83. Etching by John Musgrove, 1810.

995. ST. WINIFRED'S WELL, Holywell, 223 x 300. Etching by George Cuitt, 1813. Published in G. Cuitt, *Etchings of Ancient Buildings,* 1816, and *Wanderings and Pencillings,* 1855.
CRO

996. ST. WINIFRED'S WELL, Holywell. 103 x 84. Line engraving. Published in T. Roscoe, *Wanderings and Excursions in North Wales,* 1836.
CRO*

997. ST. WINIFRID'S WELL, Holywell. 126 x 137. Line engraving by J. Harwood, 26 Fenchurch St., London, 16 August 1845.
CRO

998. ST. WINIFRED'S WELL, Holywell. 71 x 95. Line engraving by Newman & Co., 69 Southwark Bridge Road, 1 March 1877. Published in *Views of Mold and Neighbourhood.*

999. ST. WINEFRED'S WELL, Holywell. 140 x 101. Line engraving by T. Williams. Published in *The Land we live in.*
CRO

1000. ST. WINIFRED'S WELL, Holywell. 242 x 192. Lithograph by W. Crane, Chester.

1001. ST. WINIFRED'S WELL, Holywell, Exterior of. 80 x 90. Line engraving by Newman & Co., 48 Watling St., London.
CRO

1002. ST. WINIFRED'S WELL at Holywell in Flintshire, View of. Dedicated to Rt. Hon. Countess Fingall. 299 x 450. Line engraving by Merigot after H.F. James. Published by H.F. James, Picture Gallery, Liverpool, 1 July 1811.

1003. ST. WINEFRED'S WELL at Holywell. 179 x 238. Aquatint by T. Chapman. Published in J. Poole, *Gleanings of the Histories of Holywell, Flint, St. Asaph and Rhuddlan*, 1831.
CRO*

1004. ST. WINIFRED'S WELL, Holywell, Flintshire. 242 x 191. Lithograph. Printed by Evans & Howarth, Chester.
CRO

1005. ST. WINIFRED'S WELL, Holywell, Flintshire, Back View. 170 x 217. Lithograph by T. Bailey. Printed by J. Evans, Princess St., Chester.
CRO

1006. ST. WINIFRED'S WELL, Holywell, Flintshire, Front View. 209 x 178. Lithograph by T. Bailey. Printed by J. Evans, Princess St., Chester.
CRO

1007. ST. WINIFRED'S WELL, Interior of. 80 x 95. Line engraving by Newman & Co. Published by P.M. Evans, Holywell, in *Views of Mold and Neighbourhood.*
CRO

1008. ST. WINEFRID'S WELL, Scituate 4 miles from Flint in North Wales . . . [legend follows]. FONS SACER [top middle border]. 293 x 417. Line engraving. Franc Place *del. et scul.,* P. Tempest *Exc.* [Original state of plate, 1713, cf. nos. 1009, 1010, 1011].

1009. ST. WINEFRID'S WELL usually called Holy Well near Flint in North Wales. [Also French title: 'La Fontaine de Ste. Winefride connue sous le Nom de la Sainte Fontaine près de la Ville de Flint dans le Nord de la principauté de Galles]. 255 x 18. Line engraving. Printed for John Bowles & Son at the Black Horse in Cornhil [1753-64]. [Second state of plate, cf. nos 1008, 1010, 1011].
CRO

1010. ST. WINEFRID'S WELL usually called Holy Well near Flint in North Wales. [Also French title as 1009 above]. 256 x 415. Line engraving. Printed for R. Wilkinson, No. 58 Cornhill, London [1779-84] [Third state of plate, cf. nos. 1008, 1009, 1010].

1011. ST. WINEFRID'S WELL usually called Holy Well near Flint in North Wales. [Also French title as 1009 above]. 232 x 397. Line engraving. Printed for Robt. Sayer, Map & Printseller at ye Golden Buck in Fleet Street, [1784-94]. [Fourth state of plate,cf. nos. 1008, 1009, 1010].
CRO

1012. ST. WENEFREDE'S WELL & CHAPEL. 163 x 109. Line engraving by W. Angus after M. Griffith. Published by White & Co., 1 May 1810. Also in T. Pennant, *Tours in Wales*, 1810.
CRO

1013. ST. WINEFRED'S WELL & CHAPEL in the County of Flint, The North View of. 145 x 349. Line engraving by S. and N. Buck, 9 April 1742. Published in S. and N. Buck, *Views of all the Castles,* 1742.
CRO

1014. ST. WINEFRED'S WELL & CHAPEL in the County of Flint, The North View of. 73 x 138. Line engraving [after Buck]. Published in *A Description of England and Wales,* 1769.
CRO

1015. ST. WINEFRED'S WELL, MOSS & SEAL. 160 x 155. Line engraving by P. Mazell after M. Griffith. Published in T. Pennant, *A Tour in Wales,* 1778.
CRO

1016. SOUGHTON HALL, near Northop, North Wales, North Front of. A Seat of John William Bankes, Esqr. 120 x 175. Lithograph.
CRO

1017. SOUGHTON HALL, near Northop, North Wales, South Front of. A Seat of John William Bankes, Esqr. 120 x 176. Lithograph.
CRO

1018. TALACRE, Flintshire, N.E. View of. The Seat of Sir E. Mostyn, Bart. Thos. Jones, Archt., Chester. 152 x 250. Lithograph by Paul Gauci. Printed by Engelmann & Co., *c.* 1821.
CRO

1019. TALACRE, Flintshire. N.W. View of. The Seat of Sir E. Mostyn, Bart. Thos. Jones, Archt., Chester. 156 x 257. Lithograph by Paul Gauci. Printed by Engelmann & Co., *c.* 1821.
CRO

1020. TALACRE HALL. The Seat of Sir Edward Mostyn, Bart., As it appeard after the fire, 12 September 1827. 176 x 267. Lithograph by W. Crane, Chester.

1021. WHITEFORD CHURCH [AND] GELLI CHAPEL. 127 x 167. Line engraving by J. Barlow after M. Griffith. Published by B. & J. White, 1 January 1796. Also in T. Pennant, *History of Whiteford and Holywell,* 1796.
CRO*

1022. [WHITFORD]. FAIRY OAK [Downing]. 155 diam. Line engraving. Published in T. Pennant, *History of Whiteford and Holywell,* 1796.
CRO*

1023. [WHITFORD]. GARREG, The Pharos on. 153 x 200. Line engraving. Published by B. & J. White, 1 January 1796. Also in T. Pennant, *History of Whiteford and Holywell,* 1796.
CRO*

1024. [WHITFORD]. MAEN Y CHYFAN. 142 x 160. Line engraving by P. Mazell after M. Griffith. Published in T. Pennant, *A Tour in Wales,* 1778. Also with the title MAEN ACHWYNFAN in T. Pennant, *Tours in Wales,* 1810.
CRO*

1025. [WHITFORD]. MAEN Y CHWYFAN. 168 x 157. Lithograph. Printed by Woodall, Minshall, Oswestry.

1026. [WHITFORD]. MERTON. Mr. Parry's. 74 x 95. Line engraving by J. Barlow after M. Griffith. Published by B. & J. White, 1 January 1796. Also in T. Pennant, *History of Whiteford and Holywell,* 1796.
CRO*

1027. WHITEWELL CHAPEL in Iscoed A.D. 1828, The Old. 87 x 147. Line engraving. Published in *Archaeologia Cambrensis,* 1876.
CRO*

1028. ST. WINEFRID'S WELL, Scituate 4 miles from Flint in North Wales . . . FONS
      SACER [top middle border]. 300 x 412. Line engraving by Franc. Place. Printed
      and sold by Thos. Bakewell next ye Horn Tavern in Fleet Street, London, 1731. (cf.
      nos. 1008-11].
      CRO

1101. CORWEN. 42 x 67. Line engraving. Published by T.T. & J. Tegg, Cheapside, 1 October 1832. Also in G.N. Wright, *Scenes in North Wales,* 1833.
CRO*

1102. CORWEN. 149 x 222. Soft ground etching by J.G. Wood. Published in J.G. Wood, *The Principal Rivers of Wales,* 1813.

1103. CORWEN. [Farm yard] . 97 x 240. Lithograph by 'L', 1822.

1104. CORWEN, Glendyr Cottage. [Bridge] . 137 x 216. Lithograph by 'L', 1822.

1105. CORWEN, Merionethshire. 94 x 149. Line engraving by J.C. Varrall after H. Gastineau. Published in *Wales Illustrated,* 1830.
CRO*

1106. CORWEN, N. Wales. 70 x 89. Line engraving by Newman & Co. Published by E. Edwards, Corwen.

1107. CORWEN, N[orth] W[ales], An Ancient Stone Cross at. 225 x 340. Lithograph by 'L', 1821.

1108. CORWEN AND LLANGOLLEN on the River Dee, View between. 301 x 427. Aquatint by F. Jukes after T. Walmsley. Dedicated to E. Loveden Loveden Esq. Published by F. Jukes, 10 Howland Street, 10 May 1793. Also in T. Walmsley & F. Jukes, *Views in North Wales,* 1792-4.

1109. CORWEN, View on the Dee near. 121 x 185. Aquatint. Published by Thomas McLean, Haymarket, 1822. Also in T. McLean, *A Picturesque Description of North Wales,* 1823.

1110. CORWEN BRIDGE. 305 x 423. Aquatint by F. Jukes after T. Walmsley. Dedicated to Edwd. Williames Vaughan Salesbury, Esqr. Published by F. Jukes, 10 Howland St., [No date on imprint] . Also in T. Walmsley & F. Jukes, *Views in North Wales,* 1792-4.

1111. CORWEN BRIDGE. 303 x 427. Aquatint by F. Jukes after T. Walmsley. cf. No. 1110 but imprint reads: Published by F. Jukes, 10 Howland St., London, 10 May 1793.

1112. CORWEN, Bridge over the Dee. 65 x 90. Line engraving by Newman & Co. Published by E. Edwards, Corwen.

1113. CORWEN CHURCH. 73 x 92. Line engraving by Newman & Co. Published by E. Edwards, Corwen.

1114. CROGEN AND LLANDRILLO on the River Dee, View between. 352 x 448. Aquatint by F. Jukes after T. Walmsley. Dedicated to Clopton Prhys, Esqr. [No date on imprint] .

1115. CROGEN AND LLANDRILLO on the River Dee, View between. 304 x 426. Aquatint by F. Jukes after T. Walmsley. Dedicated to Clopton Prhys Esqr. cf. No. 1114 but imprint reads: Published by F. Jukes, 10 Howland St., London, 10 May 1793. Also in T. Walmsley & F. Jukes, *Views in North Wales,* 1792-4.

1116. CONWYD MILL near Corwens in Merioneth Shire between Llangollin and Bala. 215 x 293. Aquatint by Paul Sandby. Published by J. Boydell, Cheapside, September 1775.

1117. CONWYD MILL near Corwens in Merioneth Shire between Llangollin and Bala. 215 x 293. Aquatint by Paul Sandby. Published by P. Sandby, St. Georges Row, 1 September 1776.

1118. CUNWYD MILL, N. Wales. 244 x 320. Lithograph by J. Townshend. Published by C. Hullmandel, 1824.

1119. LLANDRILLO AND CORWEN on the River Dee, View between. 305 x 425. Aquatint by F. Jukes after T. Walmsley. Dedicated to Thomas Harris, Esqr. Published by F. Jukes, 10 Howland Street, 10 May 1793. Also in T. Walmsley & F. Jukes, *Views in North Wales*, 1792-4.

1120. PONTNEWYDD near Corwen, Merionethshire. 387 x 553. Aquatint by J. Warren after Merke. Published by T. Macdonald, Poets Gallery, 39 Fleet Street, 14 May 1814.

1121. PONT-NEWYDD over the Ceirw, near Corwen, View of. 228 x 303. Aquatint by W. Ellis after E. Pugh. Dedicated to Robert Watkin Wynne, Esqr., MP. Published by E. Pugh, 13 Bedford Street, Covent Garden, 20 July 1794.

1122. PONT NEWYDD. 150 x 224. Soft ground etching by J.G. Wood, 1812.

1123. RHAIADR CYNWYD [MILL]. 84 x 128. Wood engraving by Hugh Hughes. Published in H. Hughes, *The Beauties of Cambria*, 1823.
CL

1124. RUG near Corwen. 114 x 173. Aquatint and dry-point, 1887. Published in *Archaeologia Cambrensis*, 1887.
CRO*

BIBLIOGRAPHY

R. Ackermann, *Ackermann's New Drawing Book*, 1809.

An Account of the Principal Pleasure Tours in England and Wales, 1822.

The Antiquarian Itinerary, comprising Specimens of Architecture, Monastic, Castellated and Domestic (7 Vols.), 1815-18.

W. Angus, *The Seats of the Nobility and Gentry in Great Britain and Wales in a Collection of Selected Views*, 1787.

Archaeologia Cambrensis, 1846 to date.

J. Baker, *A Picturesque Guide through Wales and the Marches, interspersed with the most interesting Subjects of Antiquity in that Principality*, 1794-7.

T. Barker, *Thirty-two Lithographic Impressions of Landscape Scenery*, 1814.

A. Batenham, *The Traveller's Companion in a Pedestrian Excursion from Chester through North Wales*, 1825.

R. Batty, *Welsh Scenery from Drawings by Capt. Batty*, 1823.

G.J. Bennett, *A Pedestrian Tour through North Wales*, 1838.

W. Bingley, *North Wales including its Scenery, Antiquities, Customs and Sketches of its Natural History* . . . (2 vols.), 1804.

W. Bingley, *A Tour round North Wales, performed during the Summer of 1798* . . ., 1800.

A. & C. Black, *Black's Picturesque Guide through North and South Wales and Monmouth-shire*, 1851.

J. Boydell, *A Collection of Views of Gentlemen's Seats, Castles and Romantick Places in North Wales*, 1792.

J.N. Brewer, *History and Antiquities of the Cathedral Church of St. Asaph, with Engravings by J. & H.S. Storer*, 1819.

Rev. B. Broughton, *Six Picturesque Views in North Wales*, 1801.

S. & N. Buck, *Views of all the Castles . . . in the Principality of Wales*, 1742.

S. & N. Buck, *Buck's Antiquities; or Venerable Remains of above Four Hundred Castles, Palaces etc. in England and Wales, with over One Hundred Views of Cities and Chief Towns*, 1774.

J.C. Buckler, *Views of the Cathedral Churches in England and Wales . . .*, 1822.

The Builder, 1842 to date.

J.B. Burke, *A Visitation of the Seats and Arms of the Noblemen and Gentlemen of Great Britain . . .*, 1852-3.

T. Catherall, *Views in North Wales, c.* 1860.

W. Cathrall, *History of North Wales comprising a Topographical Description of the Several Counties of Anglesey, Carnarvon, Denbigh, Flint, Merioneth and Montgomery*, 1828.

W. Cathrall, *Wanderings in North Wales, a Road and Railway Guide Book*, 1851.

M.B. Clough, *Scenes and Stories Little Known . . . Chiefly in North Wales*, 1861.

T. Compton, *The Northern Cambrian Mountains, or a Tour through North Wales describing the Scenery and General Characters of that Romantic Country*, 1820.

G.A. Cooke, *A Topographical and Statistical Description of Wales: Part I, North Wales, c.* 1830.

L.S. Costello, *The Falls, Lakes and Mountains of North Wales*, 1845.

D. Cox, *A Series of Progressive Lessons intended to elucidate the Art of Landscape Painting . . .*, 1823.

W. Crane, *Picturesque Scenery in North Wales*, 1842.

G. Cuitt, *Etchings of Ancient Buildings in the City of Chester, Castles in North Wales and other Miscellaneous Subjects*, 1816.

G. Cuitt, *Wanderings and Pencillings amongst Ruins of the Olden Time*, 1855.

W. Daniell, *A Voyage Round Great Britain undertaken in the Summer of the Year 1813*, 1815.

W. Davis, *Hand-Book for the Vale of Clwyd, containing a Topographical and Historical Description of the Towns of Rhyl, Abergele, St.Asaph, Denbigh and Ruthin*, 1856.

A Description of England and Wales, containing a Particular Account of each County . . . Embellished with Two Hundred and Forty Copper Plates, 1769-70.

T. Dineley, *Account of the Official Progress of His Grace Henry, the first Duke of Beaufort through Wales in 1684*, 1888.

R. Druce, *Picturesque Sketches in North Wales . . .*, n.d.

T. Dugdale, *Curiosities of Great Britain. England and Wales Delineated*, 1854-60.

England Display'd, being a New, Complete and Accurate Survey and Description of the Kingdom of England and the Principality of Wales . . . By a Society of Gentlemen, 1769.

England Illustrated, or a Compendium of the Natural History, Geography, Topography and Antiquities, Ecclesiastical and Civil, of England and Wales . . ., 1764.

The European Magazine and London Review, 1782-1826.

J. Evans, *The Beauties of England and Wales, or Delineations, Topographical, Historical, Descriptive of each County*, 1801-15. Vol. XVII (1812) contains North Wales.

T. Evans, *Walks through Wales containing a Topographical and Statistical Description of the Principality . . .*, 1819.

T.H. Fielding, *British Castles, or a Compendious History of the Ancient Military Structures of Great Britain*, 1825.

G.J. Freeman, *Sketches in Wales, or a Diary of Three Walking Excursions in that Principality in 1823, 1824, 1825* (1826).

The Gallery of Modern British Artists, 1834.

The Gentleman's Magazine, or Monthly Intelligencer, 1731-1883.

F. Grose, *The Antiquities of England and Wales* (1776, 1786, 1797 editions).

H. Grueber, *Six Lithographic Views of Seats in the Neighbourhood of Wrexham, North Wales*, n.d.

Gweirydd ap Rhys, *Hanes y Brytaniaid a'r Cymry*, 1872-4.

Sir J. Hanmer, *Notes and Papers to serve for a Memorial of the Parish of Hanmer in Flintshire*, 1872.

J. & F. Harwood, *A Volume of Views in North Wales*, c. 1846.

J. Hemingway, *Panorama of the Beauties, Curiosities and Antiquities of North Wales*, 1839.

J. Hicklin, *Excursions in North Wales: A Complete Guide to the Tourist*, 1847.

J. Hicklin, *The Illustrated Handbook of North Wales*, 1853.

J. Hicklin, *The Ladies of Llangollen*, 1847.

Sir R.C. Hoare, *A Collection of Forty-Eight Views of Noblemen's and Gentlemen's Seats, Towns, Castles, Monasteries and Romantic Places in North and South Wales*, 1795.

J.S. Howson, *The River Dee, its History and Aspect*, 1875.

H. Hughes, *The Beauties of Cambria: Sixty Views in North and South Wales*, 1823.

C. Hulbert, *The Parlour Book of British Scenery . . .*, 1832.

C. Hulbert, *The History and Description of the County of Salop . . .*, 1837.

The Itinerant: A Select Collection of Interesting and Picturesque Views in Great Britain and Ireland . . . Engraved from Original Paintings and Drawings by Eminent Artists, 1799.

O. Jones, *Cymru: Yn Hanesyddol, Parthedegol a Bywgraphyddol*, 1875.

Jones & Co., *Wales Illustrated in a Series of Views comprising the Picturesque Scenery, Towns, Castles, Seats of the Nobility and Gentry, Antiquities, etc.*, 1830.

D. King, *The Cathedrall and Conventuall Churches of England and Wales Orthographically Delineated*, 1656.

The Lady's Magazine, or Entertaining Companion for the Fair Sex, 1770-1832.

C.H. Leslie, *Rambles around Mold, c.* 1869.

The London Magazine, or Gentleman's Monthly Intelligencer, 1732-85.

M.L. Louis, *Gleanings in North Wales with Historical Sketches*, 1854.

T. McLean, *A Picturesque Description of North Wales embellished with Twenty Select Views from Nature . . .*, 1823.

S. Middiman, *Select Views in Great Britain*, 1787.

The Modern Universal British Traveller, 1779.

J. Moore & G.J. Parkyns, *Monastic Remains and Ancient Castles in England and Wales . . .*, 1792.

F.O. Morris, *Picturesque Views of Seats of the Noblemen and Gentlemen of Great Britain and Ireland, c.* 1880.

T. Moule, *Winkle's Architectural and Picturesque Illustrations of the Cathedral Churches of England and Wales*, 1838-42.

J.P. Neale, *Views of the Seats of Noblemen and Gentlemen in England, Wales, Scotland and Ireland*, 1818-23. 2nd series, 1824-9.

Newman & Co., *Seventy-two Views of North Wales*, n.d.

Newman & Co., *Views of Mold and Neighbourhood*, n.d.

S. & G. Nicholson, *Plas Newydd and Vale Crucis Abbey*, 1824.

E. Owen, *Old Stone Crosses in the Vale of Clwyd and Neighbouring Parishes*, 1886.

E. Parry, *The Cambrian Mirror, or the Tourist's Companion through North Wales*, 1850 edition.

J. Parry, *Trip to North Wales made in 1839* (1840).

T. Pennant, *The History of the Parishes of Whiteford and Holywell*, 1796.

T. Pennant, *The Journey to Snowdon*, 1781.

T. Pennant, *A Tour in Wales*, 1778 & 1784.

T. Pennant, *Tours in Wales* (3 vols.), 1810.

G. Pickering, *Four Picturesque Views in North Wales*, n.d.

Picturesque Views of the Principal Seats of the Nobility and Gentry in England and Wales, with a Description of Each Seat, 1787-8.

J. Poole, *Gleanings of the Histories of Holywell, Flint, St.Asaph and Rhuddlan, with Statistics and Geographical Account of North Wales in General*, 1831.

E. Pugh, *Cambria Depicta: A Tour Through North Wales illustrated with Picturesque Views*, 1816.

Recollections of a Tour through North Wales, 1839.

A. Roberts, *Wynnstay and the Wynns*, 1876.

Rock & Co., *Picturesque Views in North Wales*, 1871.

T. Roscoe, *Wanderings and Excursions in North Wales*, 1836.

J. Ruskin, *Lectures on Landscape*, n.d.

G. Sael, *A Collection of Welsh Tours, or a Display of the Beauties of Wales*, 1797.

P. Sandby, *A Collection of One Hundred and Fifty Select Views in England, Scotland and Ireland*, 1781.

P. Sandby, *Twelve Views in North Wales*, 1776.

P. Sandby, *The Virtuosi's Museum, containing Select Views in England, Scotland and Ireland*, 1778.

Miss Smirke, *Six Welsh Views*, c. 1808.

W. Sotheby & J. Smith, *A Tour through Parts of Wales*, 1794.

The Stationer's Almanack (Stationers' Company's Almanack), 1825.

F. Stevens, *Views of Cottages and Farmhouses in England and Wales*, 1815.

J.S. Storer & J. Greig, *Antiquarian and Topographical Cabinet, containing a Series of Views of the most Interesting Objects of Curiosity in Great Britain*, 1807-11.

H. Taylor, *Historic Notices of the Borough and County Town of Flint*, 1883.

D.R. Thomas, *A History of the Diocese of St.Asaph*, 1874.

J.M.W. Turner, *Picturesque Views in England and Wales*, 1832-8.

H.J. Tweddell, *A Handy Guide to Mold and the Neighbourhood*, 1905.

G. Virtue, *The Tourist in Wales, comprising Views of Picturesque Scenery . . .*, 1835.

T. Walmsley & F. Jukes, *Views in North Wales*, 1792-4.

H. Wigstead, *Remarks on a Tour to North and South Wales in the Year 1797 . . .*, 1800.

Lloyd-Williams & Underwood, *The Archaeological Antiquities and Village Churches of Denbighshire*, 1872.

J. Williams, *Ancient and Modern Denbigh, A Descriptive History of the Castle, Borough and Liberties*, 1856.

B. Willis, *A Survey of the Cathedral Church of St. Asaph and the Edifices belonging to it*, 1720.

R. Wilson, *Six Lithographic Drawings*, 1828.

J.G. Wood, *The Principal Rivers of Wales Illustrated . . . consisting of a Series of Views from the Source of each River to its Mouth, accompanied by Descriptions . . .*, 1813.

J.G. Wood, *Six Views in the Neighbourhood of Llangollen and Bala*, 1793.

Wrexham Registrar and Literary Miscellany, 1848-9.

G.N. Wright, *Scenes in North Wales with Historical Illustrations, Legends and Biographical Notices,* 1833.

H.P. Wyndham, *A Tour through Monmouthshire and Wales, made in the months of June and July 1774, and in the months of June, July and August 1777* (1781).

Davies: James, 977; Robert, 881, 928
Davies-Cooke, Philip: 782
Davis, W.: 86, 156, 178, 380, 389-90, 402, 405, 630, 666, 872, 897, 922
Day: 216; W., 202
Day & Haghe: 13, 67-8, 242, 245, 429, 532, 716, 827
Day & Son: 46, 161, 221, 229, 399-401, 500, 539, 823, 851-2, 893, 895-6, 978
Dayes, Edward: 90, 186, 286, 333, 617
Dee, River: Acrefair on, 3; at Erbistock, 132-4; estuary, 655; near Pen-y-Lan, 318; scene on, 56; near Valle Crucis, 470; viaduct, 57, 226-9, 232-3; views on, in Llangollen-Corwen area, 1108-9, 1114-15, 1119; waterfalls, 211, 419
  see also Bridges; Llangollen, Vale of; Pontcysyllte Aqueduct
Deeley, J.: 215
Denbigh: 58-63, 65-6, 69, 72-3, 104; abbey, 74; Burgess Tower, 64; castle, 47, 75-104, 565; castle gateway, 93-6; St. David's (old) church, 564; St. David's (new) church, 67; St.Marcellus (Whitchurch), 71; Goblin Tower, 562; Gwaenynog, 153; High Cross, 105; hospital, 68-9; Royal Bowling Green, 563
Derwen: church, 106; cross, 106
Dibdin, T.C.: 932
Dickenson, J.: 439
Dickinson, W. Robert: 11, 184, 200, 439, 648
Dinas Brân, Llangollen: 107-29, 251-2; Crow Castle, 234
Dineley, Thomas: 816-17
Disgynfa, Afon: Pistyll Rhaeadr, 327-37
Dispensary, Wrexham: 538
Douglas, John: 779, 826, 933
Douglas & Fordham, architects: 707
Douglas & Co., cotton manufacturers: 768
Downing, Whitford: 656-8, 661; Fairy Oak, 1022; grounds, 660; mill, 659
Druce, Randall: 219, 300, 418, 422, 426-8, 431
Dugdale, Thomas: 362
Dungannon, Viscount: 12-14
Dyffryn Aled, Llansannan: 130-1
Dyserth: 662-4; castle, 665; waterfall, 666

Easton, Edward: 276, 503
Edwards, E.: 375, 1106, 1112-13
Eglwysbach: Bodnant (Bod-nod), 8
Eliseg, Pillar of: 321-6
Ellesmere Canal: Chirk Aqueduct, 16-20; Ffrwd branch (Caergwrle Castle), 647; Pontcysyllte Aqueduct, 266, 356-68
Ellis, William: 7, 183, 318, 419, 787, 1121
Elwy, River: view on, 667
Emes, J.: 155
Engelmann & Co.: 20, 364, 935-7, 1018-19
Engelmann, Graf, Coindet & Co.: 5, 154, 414, 541, 737
Erbistock: church, 132-3; mill, 134
Erddig, Wrexham: 135-40
Evans: 26, 41, 136-7, 140, 546-7, 554; John, 436; J., 33, 102, 205, 218, 273, 297, 332, 350, 462-3, 499, 659, 695, 1005-6; P.M., 1007; T., 28, 407, 919; William, 6, 298-9, 417, 641, 717-18, 728-9
Evans & Gresty: 776

Evans & Howarth: 1004
Ewloe: castle, 668-9
Eyarth, Llanfair Dyffryn Clwyd: 141-2
Eyton, John Wynn: 777

Fairy Oak, Downing: 1022
Falkener, Edward: 827
Farndon (Holt) Bridge: 165
Fernal, J.: 531
Ferrey, B.: 533
Fielding: C.V., 917; Theodore Henry, 27, 79, 261, 678-9, 917
Finch, Mrs. Charles: 508
Finden, Edward: 60, 95, 192, 249, 365, 445, 479, 518, 871
Fingall, Countess: 1002
Fittler, James: 284
Fitzmaurice, Thomas: 302-3, 305-7
Flint: 670-2; castle, 673-706; church, 713, (pre-1848), 708-12; Cornist, 707; market, 716; (Old) Town Hall and stocks, 714; (New) Town Hall, 715-16
Francia, L.: 282
Frank, W.A.: 195, 420
Freeman, G.J.: 118
Friaries: Denbigh Abbey, 74; Rhuddlan Priory, 881
Fryer, W.D.: 10
Fulljames, Thomas: 68
Ffrwd: Ellesmere Canal branch (Caergwrle Castle), 647

G.H.: 565
G.S.: 828
Garreg, Whitford: Pharos, 1023
Garthewin, Llanfair Talhaearn: 143
Gastineau, Henry: 18, 36, 61, 91, 120, 162, 164, 208, 210, 254, 291, 296, 301, 351, 366, 372, 382, 388, 397, 465, 514, 530, 558, 606, 618, 645, 665, 670, 682, 742, 791, 825, 831, 858, 938, 955, 987, 1105
Gauci, Paul: 525, 637-8, 782, 889, 935-6, 1018-19
Gee, Thomas: 69-70, 81, 89
Gelli Chapel, Whitford: 1021
George IV (Prince of Wales): 155, 238
George, D.: 435, 474
Gilks: Edward, 212; Thomas, 212, 288, 353, 421, 853, 926
Girtin, Thomas: 27, 678
Glan-y-Wern, Llandyrnog: 144
Glendyr Cottage, Corwen: 1104
Glyn-diffwys: *see* Pont y Glyn-diffwys
Glynne: Sir John, 757; Sir Stephen Richard, 745, 755
Goblin Tower, Denbigh: 562
Godfrey: B., 984-5; J., 446; Richard, 602-3, 744, 758-9
Graf & Soret: 637-8, 782
Greathatch, W.: 914
Gredington, Hanmer: 717-18
Green: Benjamin, 760; J., 352; W., 688, 710
Greenfield, Holywell: brass mills, 720; Greenfield Hall, 721; smelting works, 719
  see also Holywell
Greenwood: C.J., 8, 14, 144, 163, 177, 316, 355, 408, 413, 642-3, 745, 777, 819, 841; C. & J., 946

King's Head Hotel, Llangollen: 237
Kinmel Park, Abergele: 175
Kinnerton Lodge: 776
Knight, J.B.: 373
Kronheim & Co.: 950
Kollmann, E.: 501

L.: 1103, 1107
Lacey, S.: 19, 214, 231, 558, 620, 670, 682, 825, 923
Laporte, John: 127, 235, 271
Laurie & Whittle: 327
Lawrie, C.: 860
Leeswood: 777; gates, 778
Leete, the: 790
Leigh, S.: 545
Leitch, W.L.: 13
Le Keux, John Henry: 180, 406, 621, 761, 774
Leo, Daniel: 182
Lerpinière, Daniel, 459, 476
Leslie, C.H.: 788, 799, 806
Lewis (Lewes), D.Ll.: 88, 104, 666, 857, 859, 885, 900-3, 905, 912
Lewis: B., 904; F.C., 556; I. (J.), 65, 328, 386, 662, 928
Lighthouse, Point of Ayr: 839
Liverpool Corporation: 302
Lizars, W. Home: 850, 886
Lockwood, Alfred, 793; Philip C., 793
Loggerheads: 783-4
Longman & Co.: 696, 839
Longman & Rees: 333
Lord, Joseph: 960
Louis, M.L.: 509
Loveden, E. Loveden: 1108
Luxmo(o)re: John (Bishop of St.Asaph), 952; Misses, 637-8
Lydon, Frank: 544

Llanasa: Gyrn, 724-5; Point of Ayr lighthouse, 839; Talacre, 1018-20
Llanbedr Dyffryn Clwyd: 183; Griffin Hotel, 176; Llanbedr Hall, 177-8
Llandrillo-yn-Edeyrnion: views on Dee near, 1114-15, 1119
Llandrillo-yn-Rhos: Bryn Euryn, 179; church, 53, 179-80
    see also Colwyn Bay
Llandyrnog: Glan-y-Wern, 144
Llanddulas church, 181
Llanelwy: see St. Asaph
Llanfair Dyffryn Clwyd: Eyarth, 141-2
Llanfair Talhaearn: Garthewin, 143
Llanfwrog: 183, Pool Park, 380
Llangar: Cynwyd mill and waterfall, 1116-18, 1123
Llangollen: 184-99, 202-8, 212-14, 220-1; birch trees, 200-1, 235; bridge, 236-52; church, 253-5; Dee viaduct, 57, 226-9, 232-3; Dinas Bran (Crow Castle), 107-29, 234, 251-2; fall on Dee near, 211; King's Head Hotel, 237; mill, 216; mill house, 209; old mill near, 219; parsonage, 256; Pentrefelin, 315; Plas Newydd, 338-54; Pontcysyllte Aqueduct, 266, 356-68; Trevor Hall, 417; Vale of, 210, 215, 217, 221-31, 234-5, 257-66, 312; views on Dee near, 218, 1108
Llangwm: Pont y Glyn-diffwys, 371-9

Llannerch, Trefnant: 182
Llannerch Panna, Penley: 779
Llanrhaeadr-ym-Mochnant: Pistyll Rhaeadr, 327-37
Llanrhaeadr-yng-Nghinmeirch: Llanrhaeadr Hall, 268-9
Llanrwst: 274, 277-8; bridge, 270-3, 275-6, 282-93; church, 294-6; Vale of, 279-80; Victoria Hotel, 281
Llansannan: Dyffryn Aled, 130-1
Llansilin: church, 297
Llantysilio: Britannia Inn, 418; church, 301; farm house, 300; Llantisilio Hall, 298-9; Pillar of Eliseg, 321-6
    see also Valle Crucis Abbey
Lleweni, Trefnant: bleach works, 302-4; Lleweni Hall, 305-7
Lloyd: E.H., 31, 42-4, 99, 107, 110, 168-9, 325, 453, 491, 651; Llewelyn, 841
Lloyd-Williams, E.: 64, 93, 149, 490
Llwynegrin, Mold: 780-2

M.E.P.: 723, 836
Macdonald, T.: 1120
McGahey, John: 346
Mackenzie: F., 774; William, 687
McKewan, D.H.: 212
McLean, Thomas: 48, 679-80, 1109
Maclure & Co.: 416
Maclure, Macdonald & Macgregor: 93, 317, 793, 828
McLean & Co.: 510
McQueen: 696
Macgregor, A.: 64, 93, 149, 416, 828
Madocks, John Edward: 144
Maen Achwyfan, Whitford: 1024-5
Maes Garmon, Mold: 799, 800
Malton, T.: 302
Marford: Lower Mill, 381
Markets: Flint Market, 716; Mold Market Hall, 793; Ruthin Market Place, 389
Marsh, C.: 56, 311, 371
Marshall, Charles: 234, 462
Mason, J.: 231, 620, 923
Massie, Sidney: 381, 672, 709
Mather, Thomas Trevor: 837
Matthews, T.: 833
Mawman, J.: 377
Mazell, Peter: 25, 166, 174, 313, 321, 494, 646, 979, 1015, 1024
Medland, Thomas: 136-7, 140
Merigot: 1002
Merke: 1120
Mersey, River: 655
Mertyn, Whitford: 1026
Metcalf: 84, 865, 980
Middiman, Samuel: 9, 265
Miller, William: 122, 846, 930
Mills: Cynwyd, 1116-18, 1123; Denbigh, 66; Downing, 659; Erbistock, 134; Llangollen, 209, 216, 219; Pentrefelin (Llangollen), 315; Rossett (Marford), 381; Ruthin, 406
Minshall, Miss W. Wynne: 283
Minshull & Hughes: 736
Moel Famau: 785-90; Jubilee Monument, 788-9
Mold: 790-2; Bailey Hill, 799; church, 799, 804-12; Gwysaney, 723; Hallelujah Monument, 795; High Street, 796-8; Leeswood,

Topham, F.W.: 469
Tower, Mold: 802
Townshend, James: 135, 145, 1118
Trefnant: church, 416; Llannerch, 182;
    Lleweni, 302-7
Trelawnyd (Newmarket): Clwyddian Hills
    from, 652
Tremeirchion: Bachegraig, 601-3; Brynbella,
    639-40
Trevalyn Hall, Allington: 413-15
Trevor Hall, Llangollen: 417
Tunbridge, T.: 207
Turner: James Mallard William, 213, 466, 671,
    686, 696; William, 676
Tweddell, H.J.: 783, 789-90, 796, 800, 808
Ty'n y Pistyll, Llantisilio: 418

Underwood: 64, 93, 149, 285, 490
Unger, H.W.: 755

Valle Crucis Abbey: 420-69; 471-505, 507, 561;
    ash, 506; River Dee near, 470; waterfall
    near, 419
Varley, John: 460, 843
Varrall, J.C.: 36, 208, 366, 466, 665, 1105
Vernor, Hood & Sharpe: 205, 659
Viaducts: Chirk, 46; Dee, 57, 226-9, 232-3
Victoria Hotel, Llanrwst: 281
Vincent Brooks, Day & Son: 978
Virtue, G.: 448
Voelas, Pentrefoelas: 508
Vroncyssyllte: Pontcyssyllte Aqueduct, 266,
    356-68

W.H.: 754, 762
Wales, Prince of (George IV): 155, 238
Walker: 26, 41; John, 137, 150, 186, 286,
    298-9, 417, 460, 546, 671, 728-9; John &
    Charles, 946; William, 503; W. & J., 150-1
Wallis, W.: 120, 388, 514, 530, 791, 987
Walm(e)sley, Thomas: 3, 132-4, 238, 302, 309,
    315, 383, 504-5, 830, 840, 1108, 1110-11,
    1114-15, 1119
Walter, H.: 359
Walton: J.W., 532; W., 175, 484; W.L., 352, 354
Warren, Charles T.: 953, 964, 967; J., 1120
Waterfalls: on Dee, 211; Dyserth, 666; Nant-y-
    Ffrith, 824; Pistyll Rhaeadr, 327-37; Pont
    y Glyn-diffwys, 375; Rhaeadr Cynwyd,
    1123
Waterlow & Sons: 319-20
Waterwheels: 816
Watson, Mrs.: 728-9
Watts, William: 129, 131, 303, 306-7, 529, 747,
    756, 767, 769
Webber: 116
Wehnert, F.: 716
Welch, John: 716
Wells: St.Asaph, 941; St.Winefride's, 969-1015
Welsh, Edward: 538

Wesson, J.: 874
West, Allen C.: 729
Westall, William: 726
Westley, J.: 138
Whitchurch, Denbigh: 71
White, B. & J.: 604, 657, 765-6, 817-18, 821,
    1021, 1023, 1026
White & Co.: 732, 1012
Whiteman & Bass: 181, 807, 826
Whitewell, Iscoed: chapel, 1027
Whitford: Bychton, 644; church, 1021;
    Downing, 656-8, 659-61; Fairy Oak, 1022;
    Gelli Chapel, 1021; Maen Achwyfan, 1024-
    5; Mertyn, 1026; Mostyn, 813-21; Pharos,
    1023
Whymper: 746, 752, 876
Wickes, Charles: 539
Widnell, J.: 186
Wigfair, Cefn: Chapel Vair, 509
Wigstead: H. 187; W., 187

Wilkinson: John, 11; R., 1010
Williams: E., 141-2, 189-90, 220, 308, 361, 640,
    647, 652, 654-5, 664, 667, 778, 784, 786,
    795, 803, 824, 975; John, 63, 70-1, 81,
    562-5; T., 999; William, 874; Rev. William
    Maddock, 716
Willis, Browne: 960
Willmore: Arthur, 448; James T., 213
Wilson: Richard, 202; William C., 182, 661,
    720-1, 768, 820, 879
Winkles, B.: 953, 964, 967
Wood, John George: 58, 165, 188, 204, 211,
    239-40, 264, 274, 310, 344, 360, 379, 384,
    471, 607, 613, 677, 733, 844, 916, 1102,
    1122
Woodall, Minshall: 105, 1025
Woodall & Venables: 283
Woods, John: 701
Woolnoth, W.: 273, 350
Worthenbury: Broughton Hall, 636
Wrexham: 510-12, 514-19; Acton, 4-6; church,
    520-37, 539; dispensary, 538; Erddig, 135-
    40; Grove Park School, 517; Mount Street,
    518-19; Pentre'r Felin, 513
Wright: G.N., 29, 62, 80, 266, 295, 339, 385,
    391, 447, 542, 683, 734, 815, 848, 920,
    976, 1101; I., 611
Wrightson, J.: 684, 687, 875, 877, 921
Wyatt: J. Dayton, 911; T.H., 823
Wyndham, H.P.: 276, 503
Wynne, Sir John: 283
Wynn(e): Robert Watkin, 1121; Sir Watkin
    Williams, 419, 437, 528, 548, 552-5, 557-8;
    Colonel, 143
Wynnstay: 540-58; Acrefair near, 3; Nant-y-
    belan, 264, 308-12; Wynnstay Park, 559-60;
    views from Park, 45, 230-1

York(e): Philip, 130-1; Simon, 135, 139